BON JOVI ★ BOU

WWW.BONJOVI.COM

Transcribed by HEMME LUTTJEBOER

Project Managers: JEANNETTE DeLISA and AARON STANG
Music Editor: COLGAN BRYAN Technical Editor: JACK ALLEN
Book Art Layout: MARTHA L. RAMIREZ Album Art: © 2002 THE ISLAND DEF JAM MUSIC GROUP
Photography: KEVIN WESTENBERG Album Art Direction: KEVIN REAGAN
Album Design: KEVIN REAGAN, BRET HEALEY

Exclusive Distributors:
Music Sales Limited, 8/9 Frith Street, London W1D 3JB, England.
Music Sales Pty Limited, 120 Rothschild Avenue, Rosebery, NSW 2018, Australia.
Order No. AM976448 ISBN: 0-7119-9822-1
www.musicsales.com

BON JOVI ★ BOUNCE

BOUNCE

BOUNCE

BOUNCE

BOUNCE

UNDIVIDED 9
EVERYDAY 15
THE DISTANCE 21
JOEY 27
MISUNDERSTOOD 37
ALL ABOUT LOVIN' YOU 44
HOOK ME UP 50
RIGHT SIDE OF WRONG 56
LOVE ME BACK TO LIFE 63
YOU HAD ME FROM HELLO 69
BOUNCE 77
OPEN ALL NIGHT 82

BOUNCE

UNDIVIDED

Words and Music by
JON BON JOVI, RICHIE SAMBORA and BILLY FALCON

D5
E5 F5
D5
F5 E5
D5
E5 F5
those were our chil - dren, that was our fa - thers, that was each of us. A
songs you si - lenced, deep down it's ring - ing out in each of us.
hold
Cont. in slashes
*Dbld. by Elec. Gtr. 3.
1.
G5
Bb6
*Elec. Gtrs. 2 & 3
mil - lion prayers to God a - bove, a mil - lion tears make an o -
*Composite arrangement.
To Next Strain (To Chorus:)
open
2.
G5
- cean of... Yeah, yeah, yeah, yeah, yeah.
Chorus:
D5
Bb5
F5
C5
Rhy. Fig. 2
One for love. one for
Rhy. Fig. 2A
Elec. Gtr. 4 (w/dist.)
mf

D5
B♭5
F5
truth; one for me, one
w/Rhy. Figs. 2 (Elec. Gtrs. 2 & 3) & 2A (Elec. Gtr. 4) simile
C5
1.
2.3.
D5
B♭5
end Rhy. Fig. 2
for you. 2. I you. Where we once were di - vid -
end Rhy. Fig. 2A
F5
C5
B♭5
- ed, now we stand u - nit - ed. We stand as one,
Guitar Solo:
w/Rhy. Fig. 2 (Elec. Gtr. 3) simile
F5
C5
To Coda
D5
B♭5
un - di - vid - ed.
Elec. Gtr. 5 (w/dist.)
mf

F5
C5
D5
T
A
B
B♭5
F5
C5
hold
Verse 3:
w/Rhy. Fig. 1 (Elec. Gtr. 1) 2 times, simile
D5
F5 E5 D5
E5 F5
D5
F5 E5
How man - y hands? how man - y hearts? how man - y dreams
D5
E5 F5 G5
Elec. Gtrs. 2 & 3
been torn a - part? E - nough, e - nough, the time

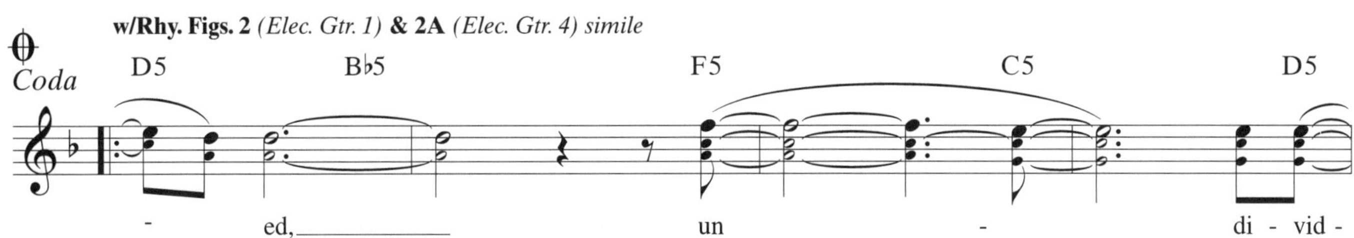

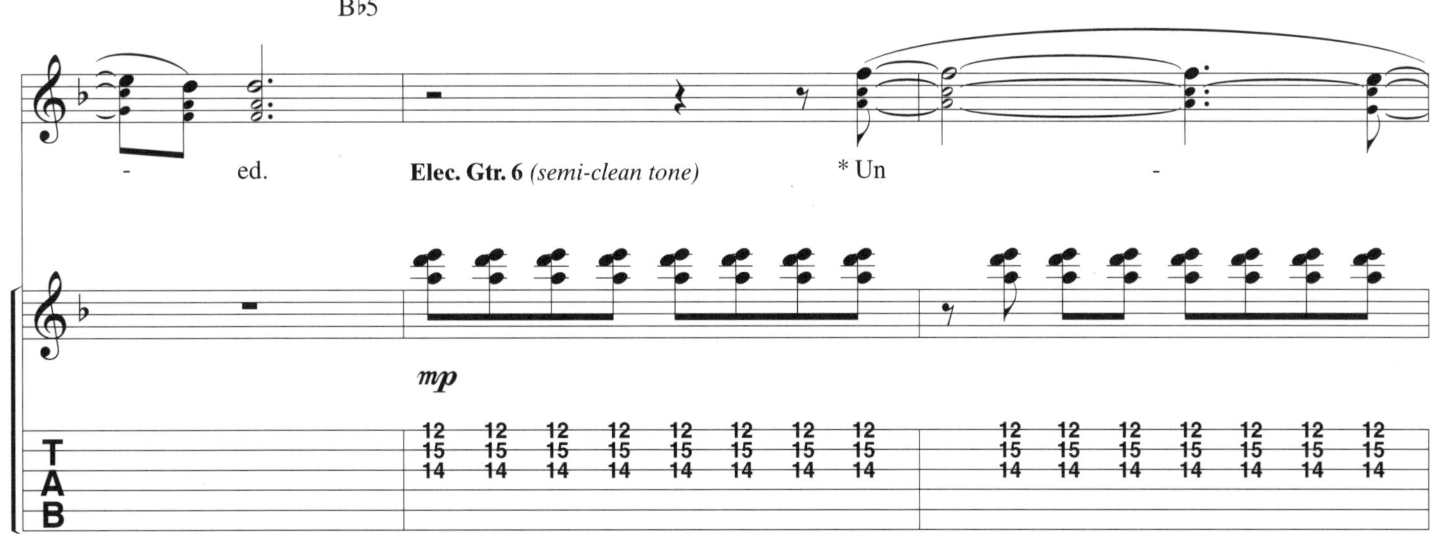

*First time only.

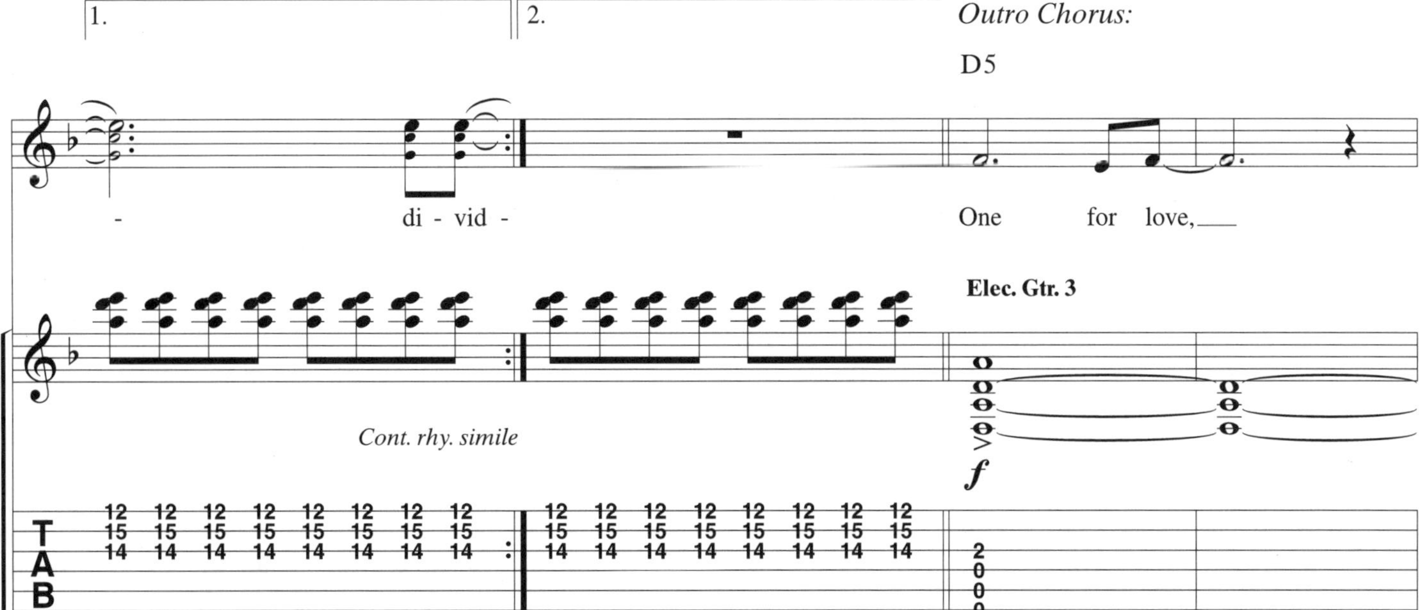

C
Dm
B♭sus2
Acous. Gtr. 1
mp
mf
open
⑥
one for truth. One for me, one
F
C
Dm
B♭sus2
Cont. rhy. simile
for you. When we once were di - vid -
T
A
B
F
C
- ed, now we stand u - nit - ed. We stand
Dm
B♭sus2
F
Dsus2
Acous. Gtr. 1
as One un - di - vid - ed.

EVERYDAY

Words and Music by
JON BON JOVI, RICHIE SAMBORA
and ANDREAS CARLSSON

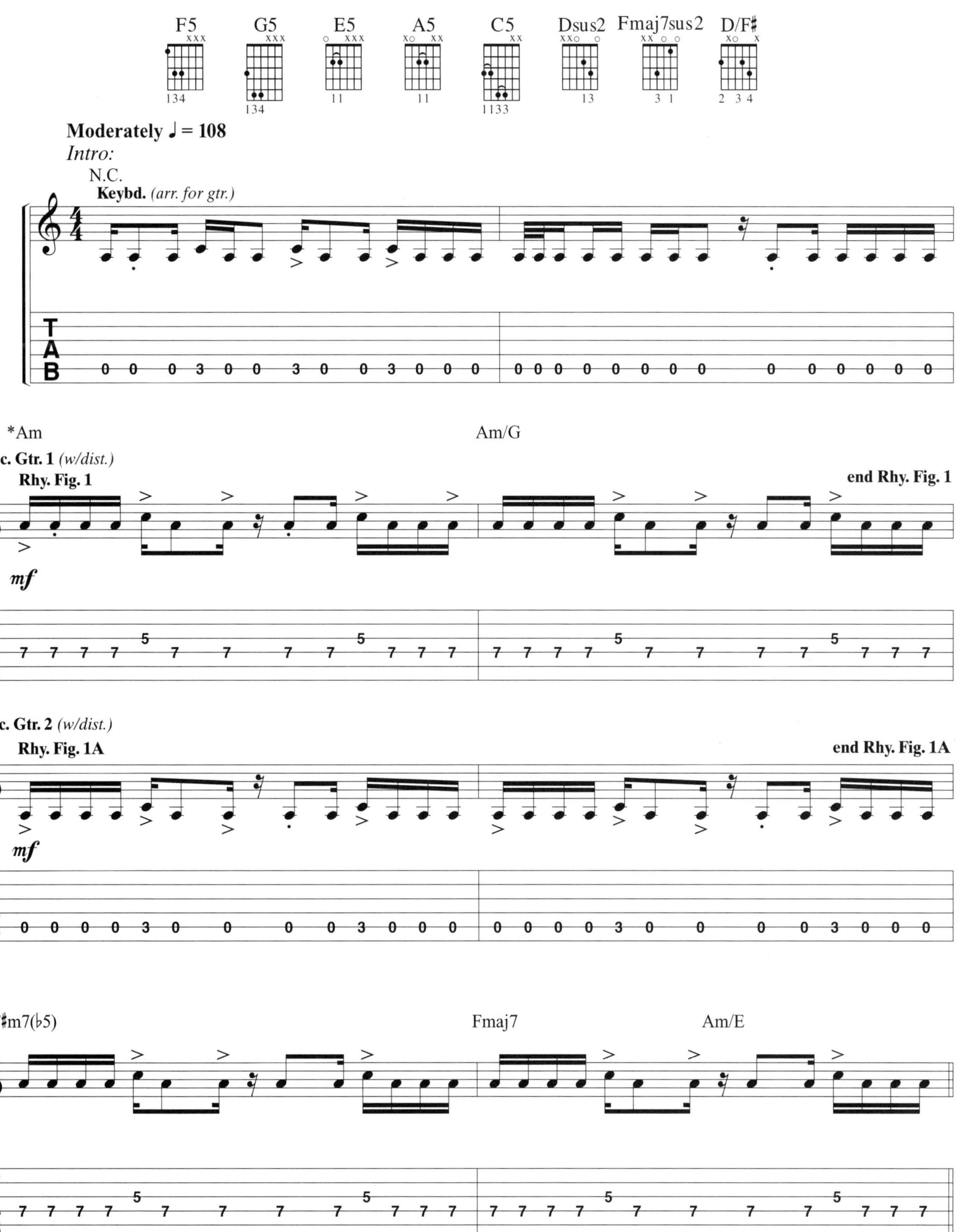

Verse:
w/Rhy. Figs. 1 (Elec. Gtr. 1) & 1A (Elec. Gtr. 2) 4 times, simile
w/Keybd. ad lib. on repeat
Am
1. I used to be the kind of guy who'd nev - er let you look in - side. I'd smile when I was cry - ing.
2. Change, ev - 'ry - bod - y's feel - in' strange, nev - er gon - na be the same. Makes you won - der how the world keeps turn - ing.
Elec. Gtr. 3 (on repeat)
I had noth - ing but a lot to lose. Thought I had a lot to prove, in my life there's no de - ny - ing.
Life, learn - ing how to live my life, learn - ing how to pick my fights, take my shots while I'm still burn - ing.
Elec. Gtr. 3 (w/dist.)
mf
w/flanger & delay effects hold throughout

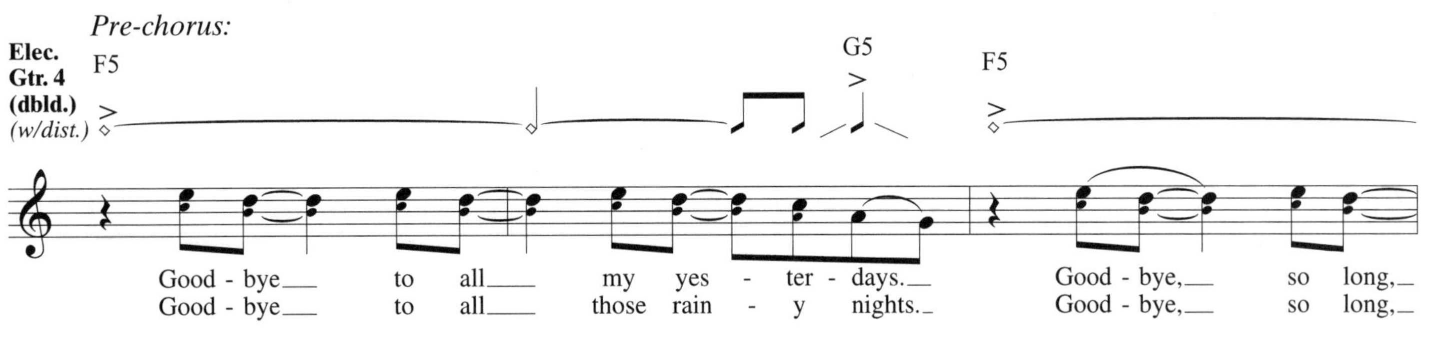
Pre-chorus:
Elec. Gtr. 4 (dbld.) (w/dist.)
F5
G5
F5
Good - bye to all my yes - ter - days. Good - bye, so long,
Good - bye to all those rain - y nights. Good - bye, so long,

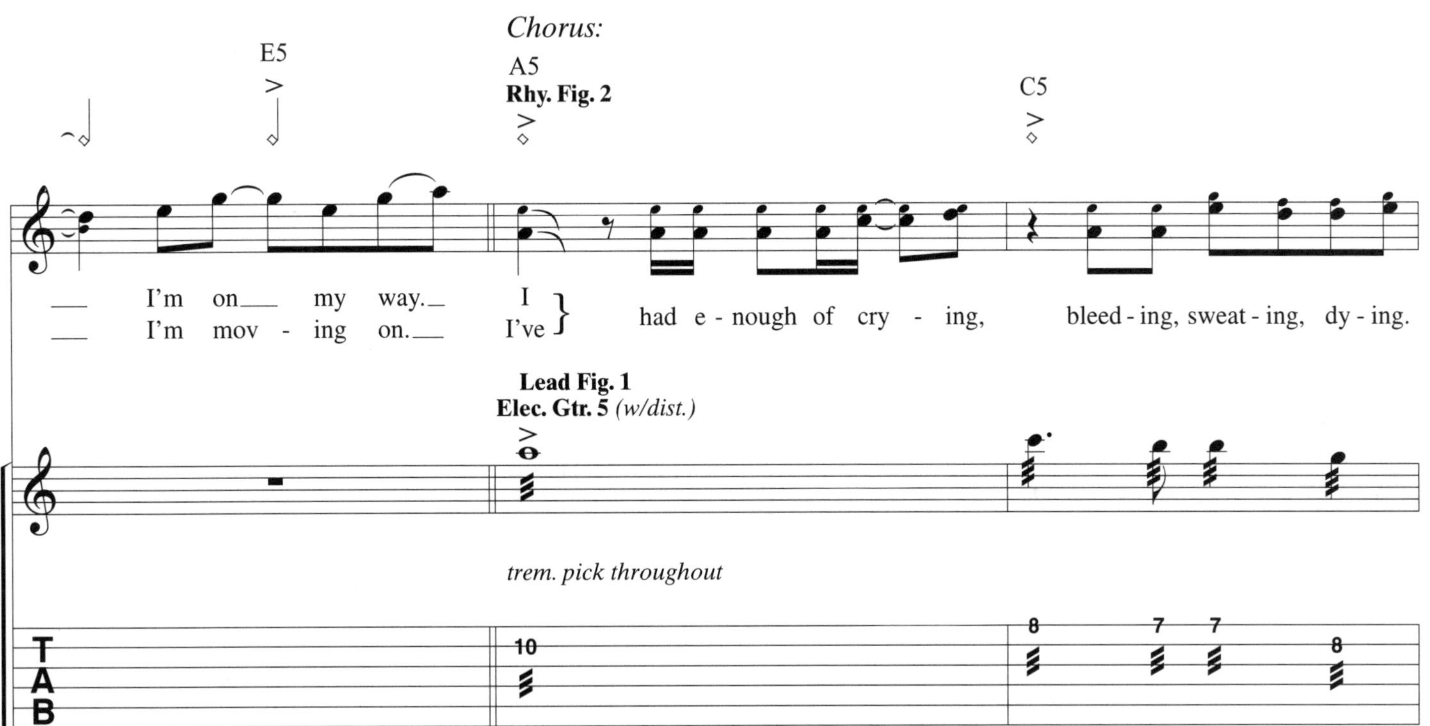
Chorus:
E5
A5
Rhy. Fig. 2
C5
I'm on my way. I
I'm mov - ing on. I've
had e - nough of cry - ing, bleed - ing, sweat - ing, dy - ing.
Lead Fig. 1
Elec. Gtr. 5 (w/dist.)
trem. pick throughout
10
8 7 7 8

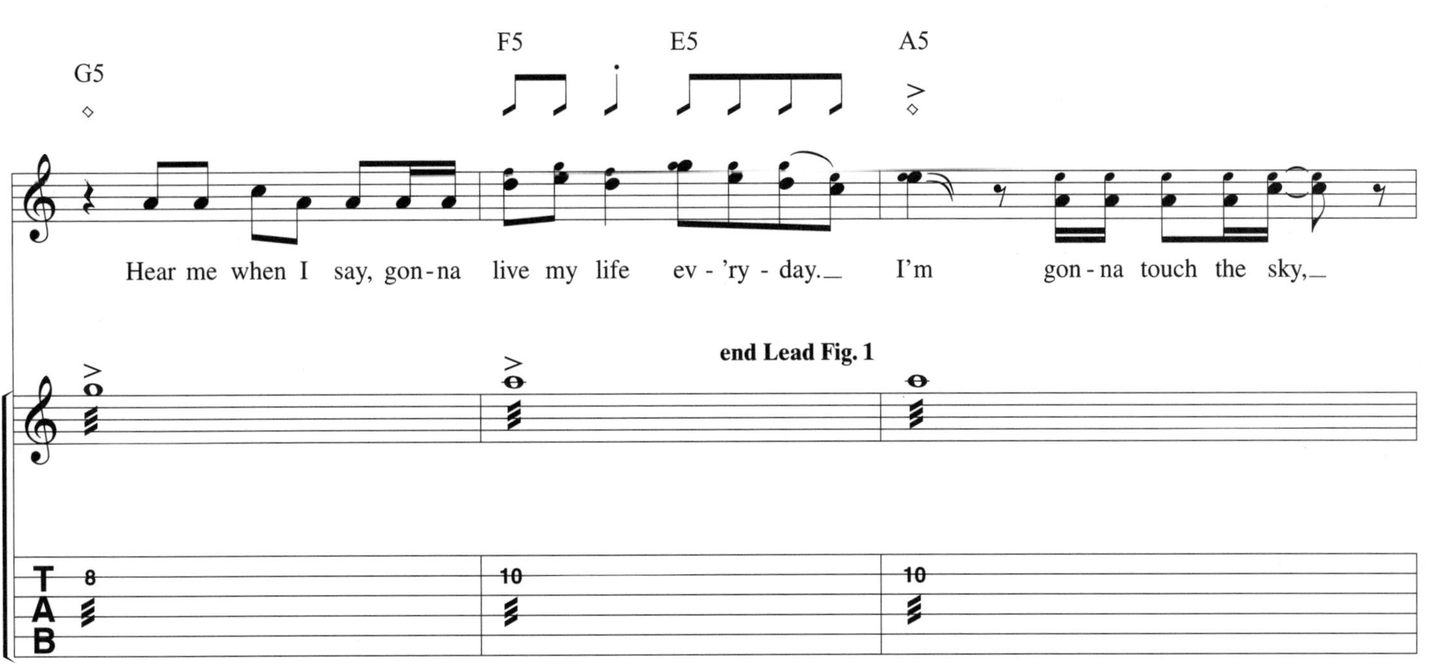
G5
F5
E5
A5
Hear me when I say, gon - na live my life ev - 'ry - day. I'm gon - na touch the sky,
end Lead Fig. 1
8
10
10

1.
C5
G5
F5
G5
end Rhy. Fig. 2
spread these wings and fly.
I ain't here to play, gon-na live my life ev-'ry-day.
2.
A5
open
1fr.
open
F5
G5
Bridge:
Dsus2
Hit the gas, take the wheel, I just
live my life ev-'ry-day.
Elec. Gtr. 3
hold throughout
Fmaj7sus2
made my-self a deal. There ain't noth-ing gon-na get in my way. Ev-'ry day.

Guitar Solo:
w/Rhy. Figs. 1 *(Elec. Gtr. 1)* **& 1A** *(Elec. Gtr. 2) 4 times, simile*

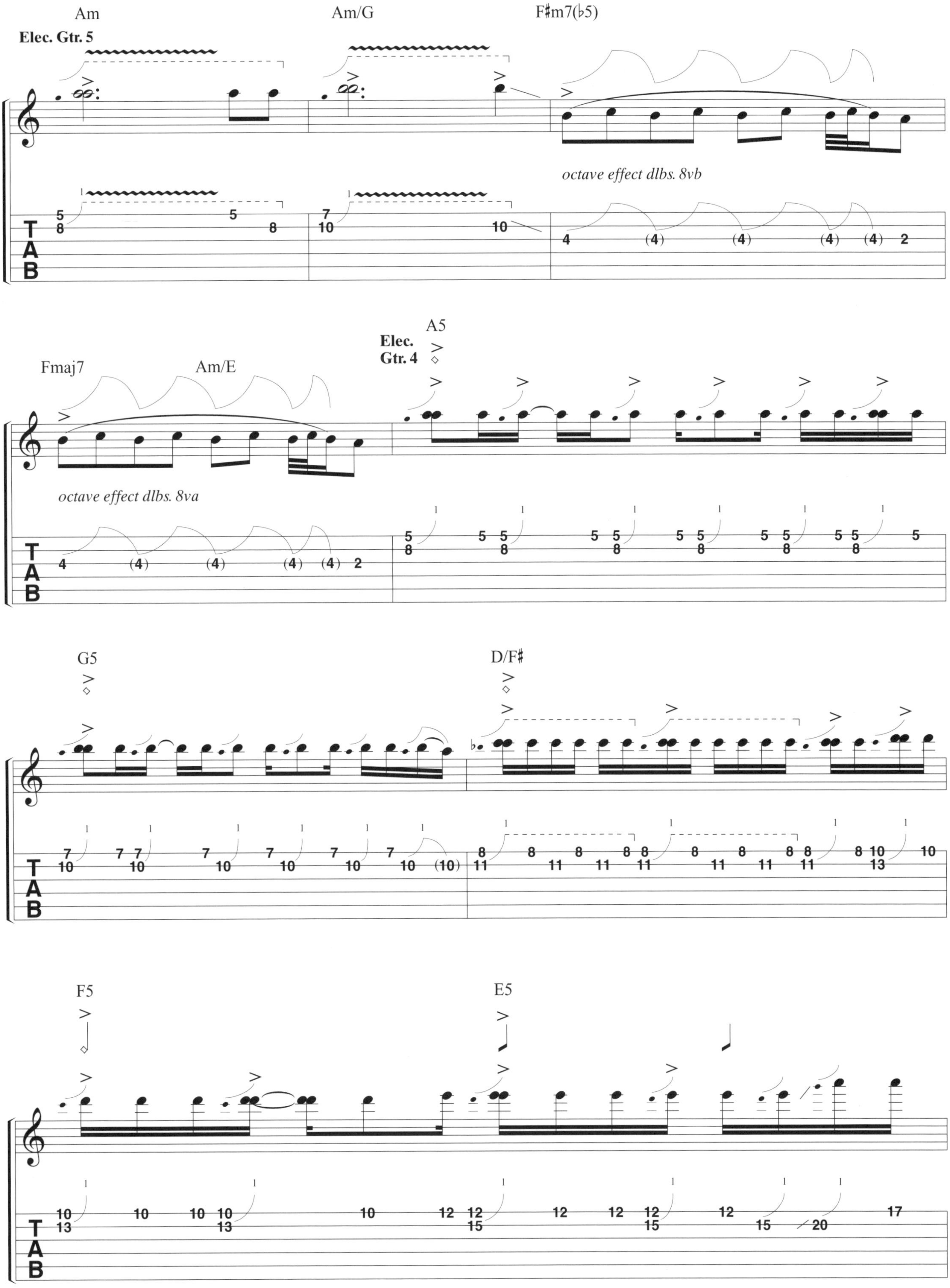

Am Am/G F♯m7(♭5)

Elec. Gtr. 5

octave effect dlbs. 8vb

Fmaj7 Am/E

Elec. Gtr. 4 A5

octave effect dlbs. 8va

G5 D/F♯

F5 E5

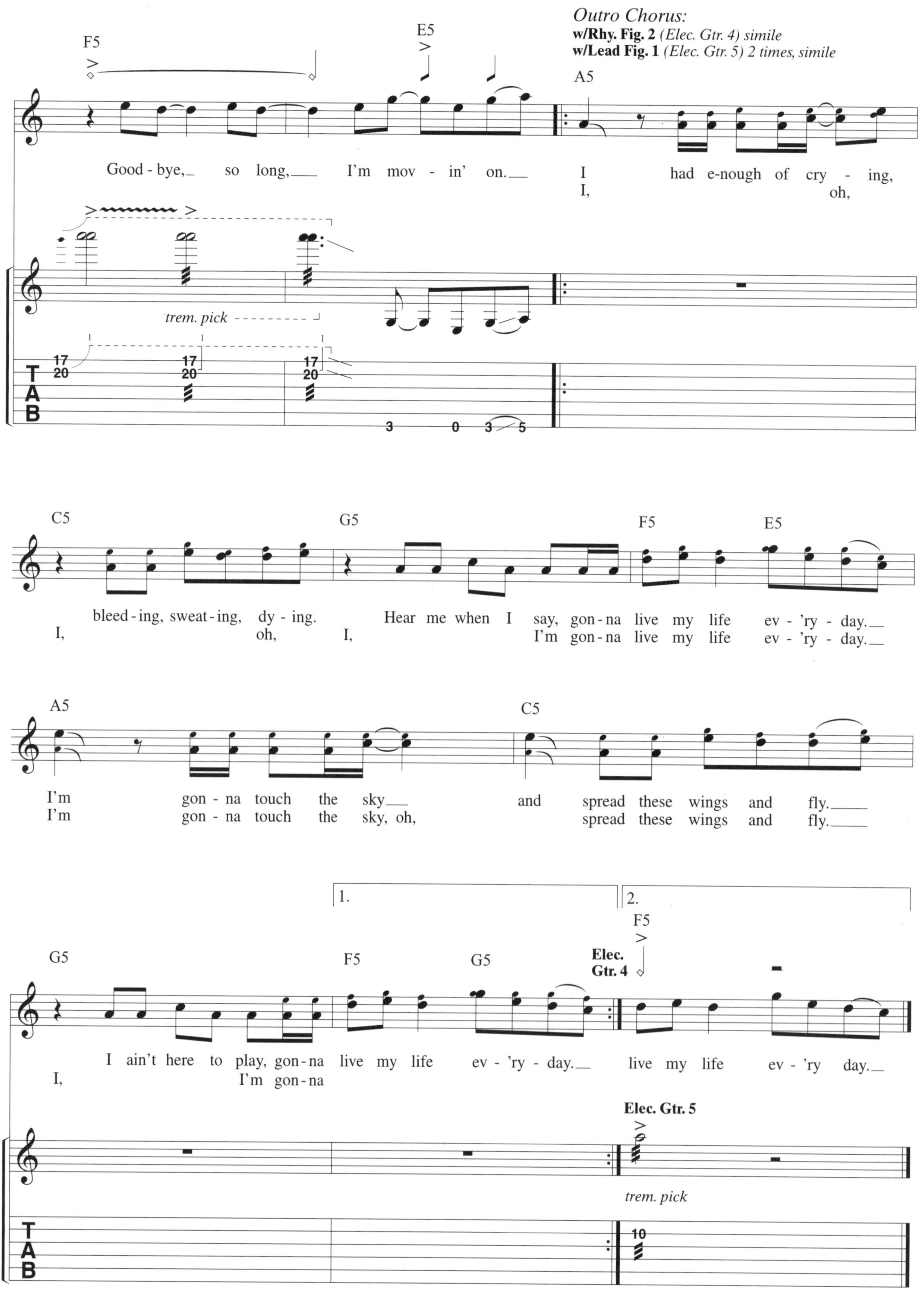

Outro Chorus:
w/Rhy. Fig. 2 (Elec. Gtr. 4) simile
w/Lead Fig. 1 (Elec. Gtr. 5) 2 times, simile
F5
E5
A5
Good - bye, so long, I'm mov - in' on.
I had e-nough of cry - ing,
I, oh,
trem. pick
C5
G5
F5
E5
bleed - ing, sweat - ing, dy - ing. Hear me when I say, gon - na live my life ev - 'ry - day.
I, oh, I, I'm gon - na live my life ev - 'ry - day.
A5
C5
I'm gon - na touch the sky and spread these wings and fly.
I'm gon - na touch the sky, oh, spread these wings and fly.
1.
2.
G5
F5
G5
F5
Elec. Gtr. 4
I ain't here to play, gon - na live my life ev - 'ry - day. live my life ev - 'ry day.
I, I'm gon - na
Elec. Gtr. 5
trem. pick

THE DISTANCE

Words and Music by
JON BON JOVI, RICHIE SAMBORA and DESMOND CHILD

All gtrs. w/Drop D tuning: ⑥ = D

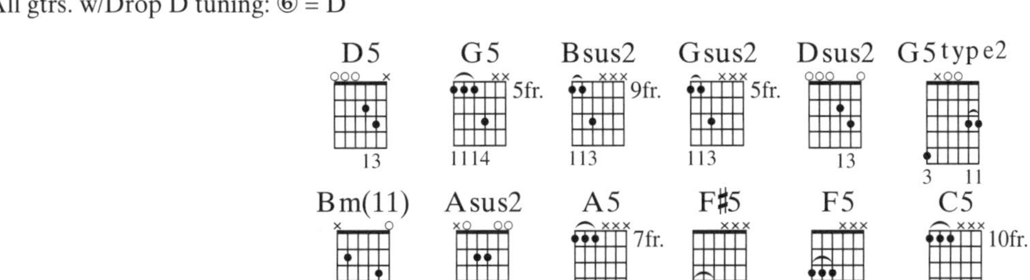

Moderate rock ♩ = 88

Intro:

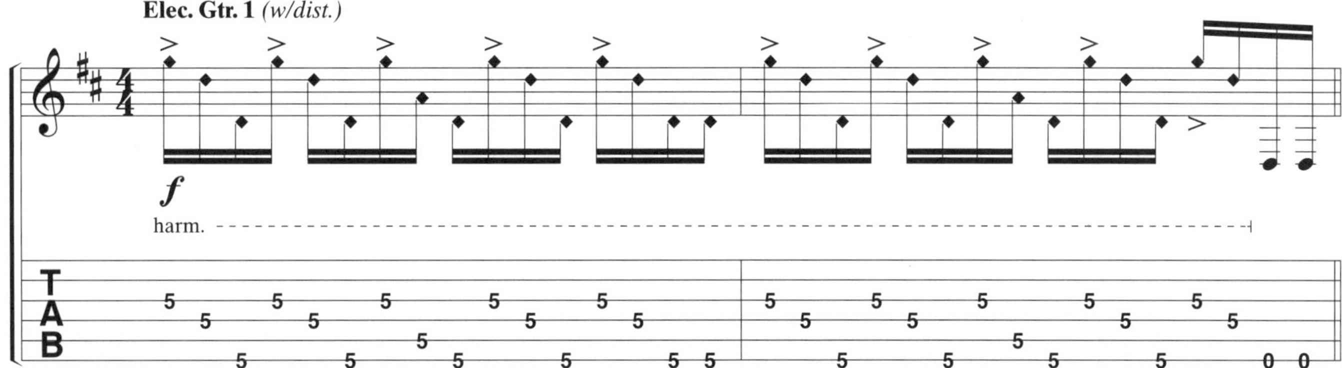

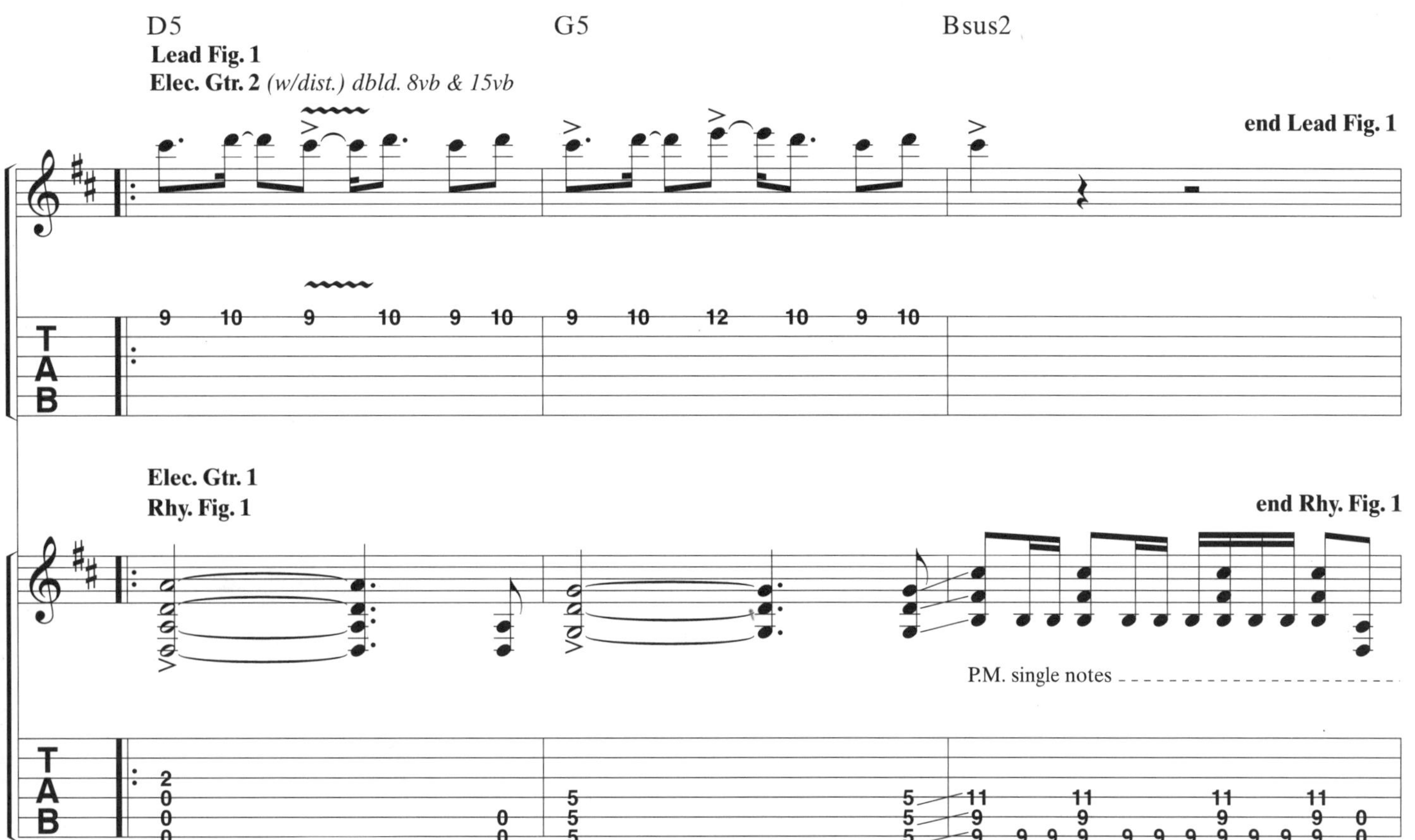

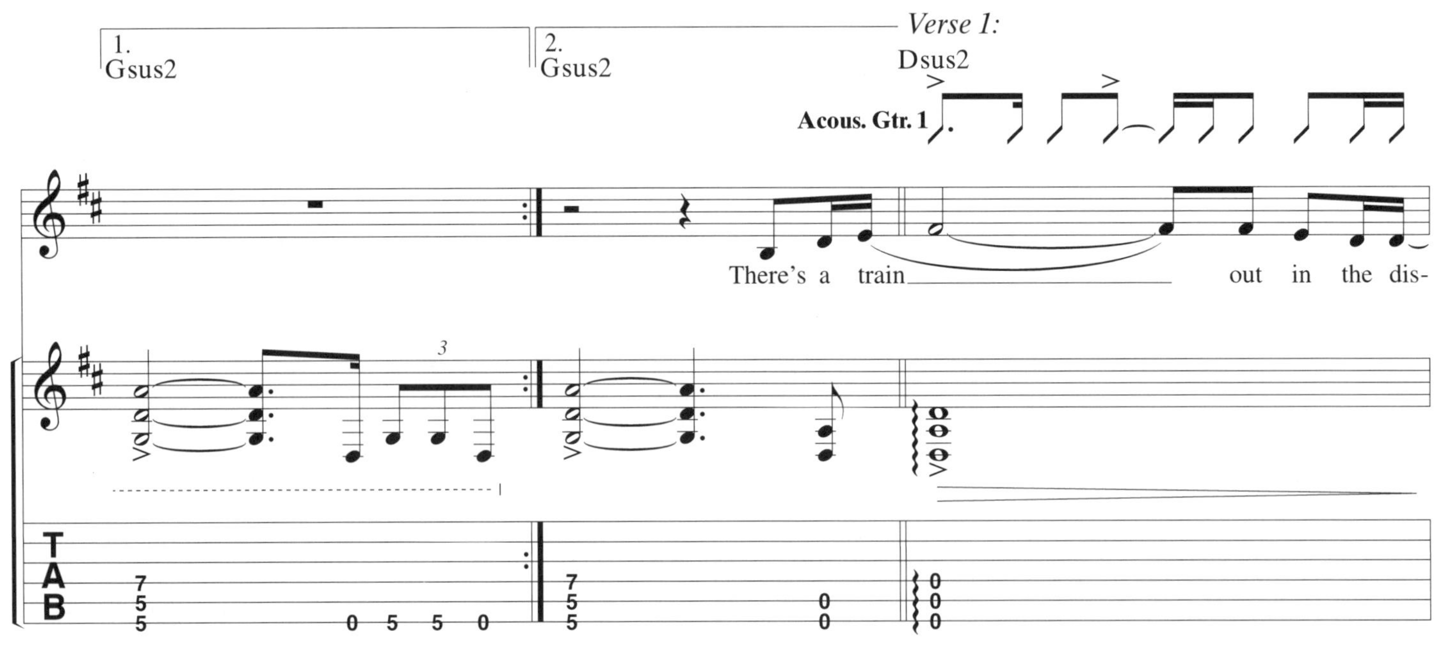
1.
Gsus2
2.
Gsus2
Verse 1:
Dsus2
Acous. Gtr. 1
There's a train out in the dis-
3
T
A
B
7
5
5
0 5 5 0
7
5
5
0
0
0
0
0

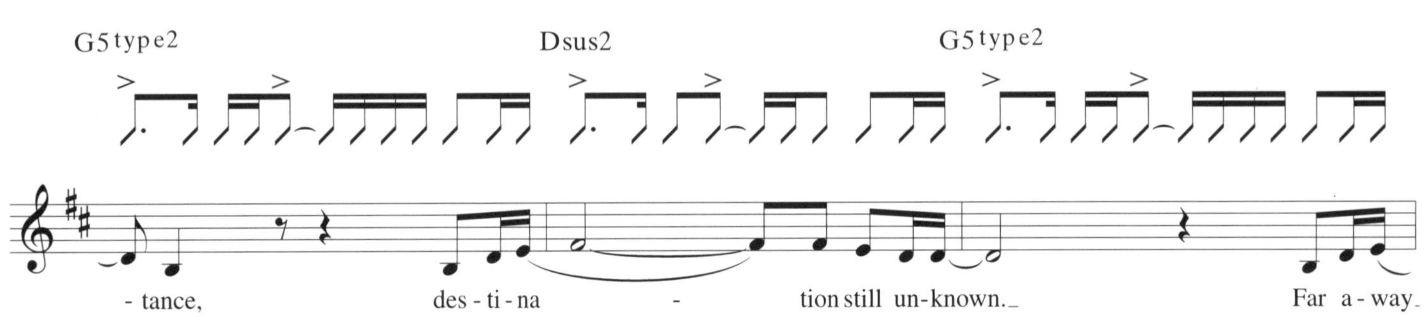
G5type2
Dsus2
G5type2
-tance, des - ti - na - tion still un-known.
Far a-way

Bm(11)
G5type2
where no one's wait - ing, so far from home, so far from home.
Elec. Gtr. 1
mp
T
A
B

Verses 2 & 3:

Dsus2

2. There's a rose ___ out - side your win -
___ that runs be - tween

Elec. Gtr. 3 *(clean-tone)*

mf

hold throughout

TAB: 15 14 0 15 14 0 15 14 15 14

TAB: 7 5 5 | 7 5 5 | 7 5 5 | 7 5 5 | 7 5 5 | 5 5 5 | 5 5 5 | 5 5 5 | 5 5 5 || 0 0 0

mf

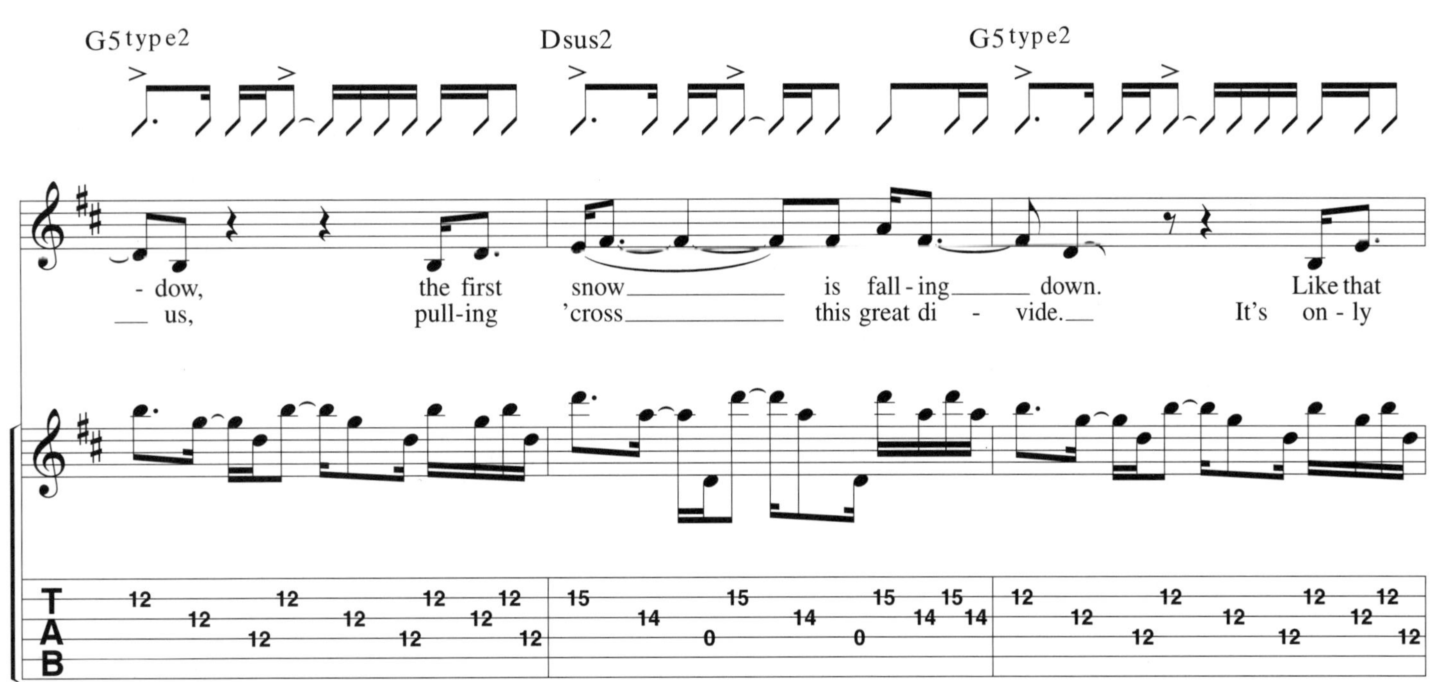

Bm(11)
Asus2
G5
Elec. Gtr. 1 (dbld. by Acous. Gtr. 1))
lone - some whis-tle blow - ing I keep on go-ing Keep on go-
there for the be - liev - ers. Don't stop be - liev-ing. Don't stop be - liev-
A5
open
Chorus:
D5
Rhy. Fig. 2
Gsus2
open
- ing.
- ing.
Close your eyes and see my blue skies break - ing through these
D5
Gsus2
open
D5
dark clouds. You are the light.
In my mind I see your
Gsus2
open
Bsus2
Gsus2
end Rhy. Fig. 2
open
red dress and your arms are reach - ing through the night. I'll
1.
w/Rhy. Fig. 1 (Elec. Gtr. 1) simile
w/Lead Fig. 1 (Elec. Gtr. 2) simile
G5 F♯5 D5 G5 F♯5 D5 G5
open
F5
D5
G5
nev - er give up the fight. I'll go the dis - tance.

Bsus2
Gsus2
D5
2.
open
F5
D5 E5 G5 C5
Elec. Gtr. 1
Cont. in notation
3. There's a thread I'll go the dis - tance,
Rhy. Fig. 3
Elec. Gtr. 1
P.M. open string throughout
B5 D5 E5 G5 C5 B5 D5
I'll go the dis - tance. There's a nev-
end Rhy. Fig. 3
Bridge:
w/Rhy. Fig. 3 (Elec. Gtr. 1) 3 1/2 times, simile
E5 G5 C5 B5 D5 E5 G5 C5
- er end - ing sto - ry that be - gins with you and I.
B5 D5 E5 G5 C5 B5 D5
Like the rose out - side your win - dow, don't let it die,

Chorus:
w/Rhy. Fig. 2 (Elec. Gtr. 1) simile
E5 G5 C5
N.C.
D5
don't let it die.
Bkgd. Vcl.: Don't let it die.
Close your eyes and see my
Elec. Gtr. 1
harm.

Gsus2
D5
Gsus2
blue skies break - ing through these dark clouds. You are the light.

D5
Gsus2
Bsus2
In my mind I see your red dress and your arms are reach - ing through the night.

1. Gsus2
2. Gsus2
G5 F♯5 D5 G5
F♯5
G5
F5
Elec. Gtr. 1
open
I'll nev-er give up the fight, I'll go the dis -

Outro:
w/Rhy. Fig. 3 (Elec. Gtr. 1) 2 times, simile
Repeat till fade
D5
E5 G5 C5
B5
D5
E5 G5 C5
B5
D5
- tance. I'll go the dis - tance. I'll go the dis -

JOEY

Words and Music by
JON BON JOVI and RICHIE SAMBORA

*All gtrs. Capo I

Esus2
1341
C♯sus2
4fr.
1341
E/B
4fr.
4 312
Dsus2
13
Etype2
4fr.
312
E
231
B
11333
C♯m
4fr.
13421
Asus2
23
A
333
F♯m7
2 333
G♯m7
2 333
F♯m(11)
2 34
G♯m7(♯5)
4fr.
2 34
Bsus
134
C♯m7
4fr.
134
B(11)/D♯
4fr.
311
D
132

Moderately ♩ = 90

Intro:
Esus2
C♯sus2
E/B
Dsus2
Asus2
Piano (arr. for gtr.)
mf hold throughout

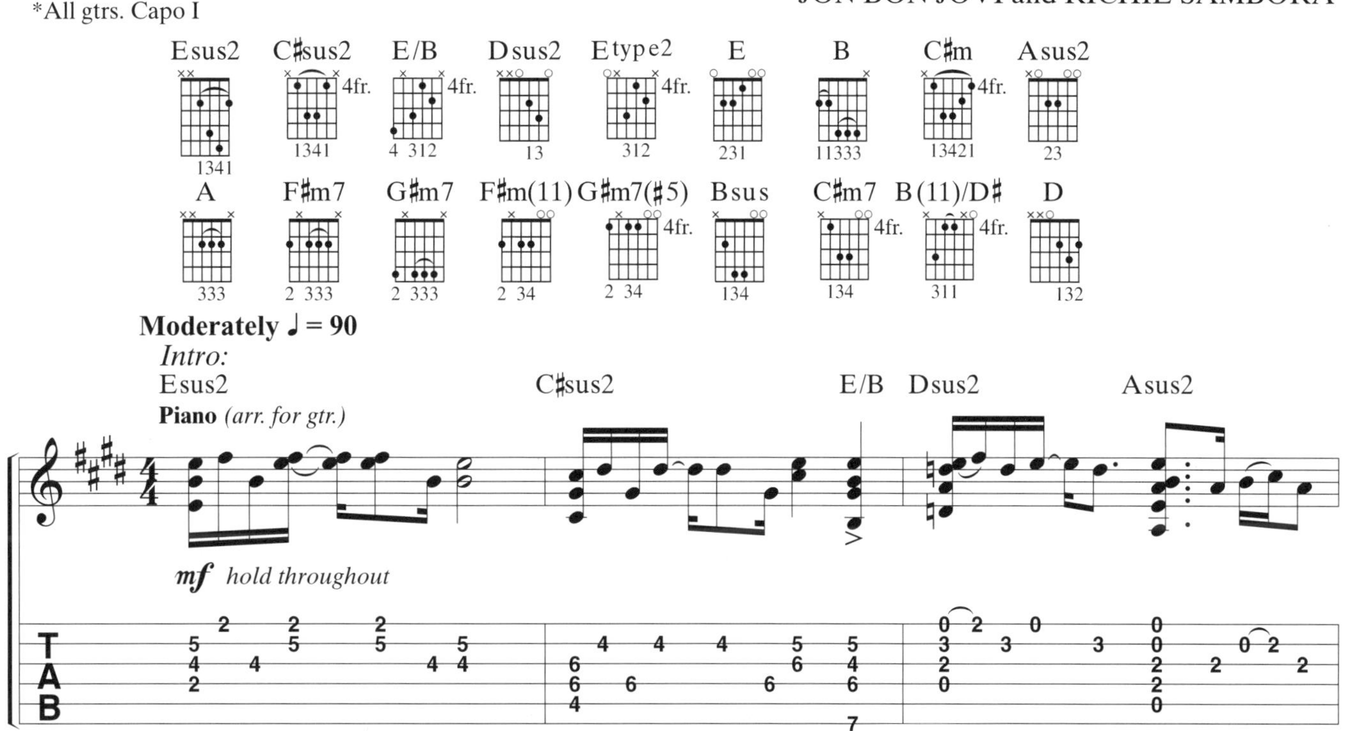

*Music sounds 1/2 step higher than written.

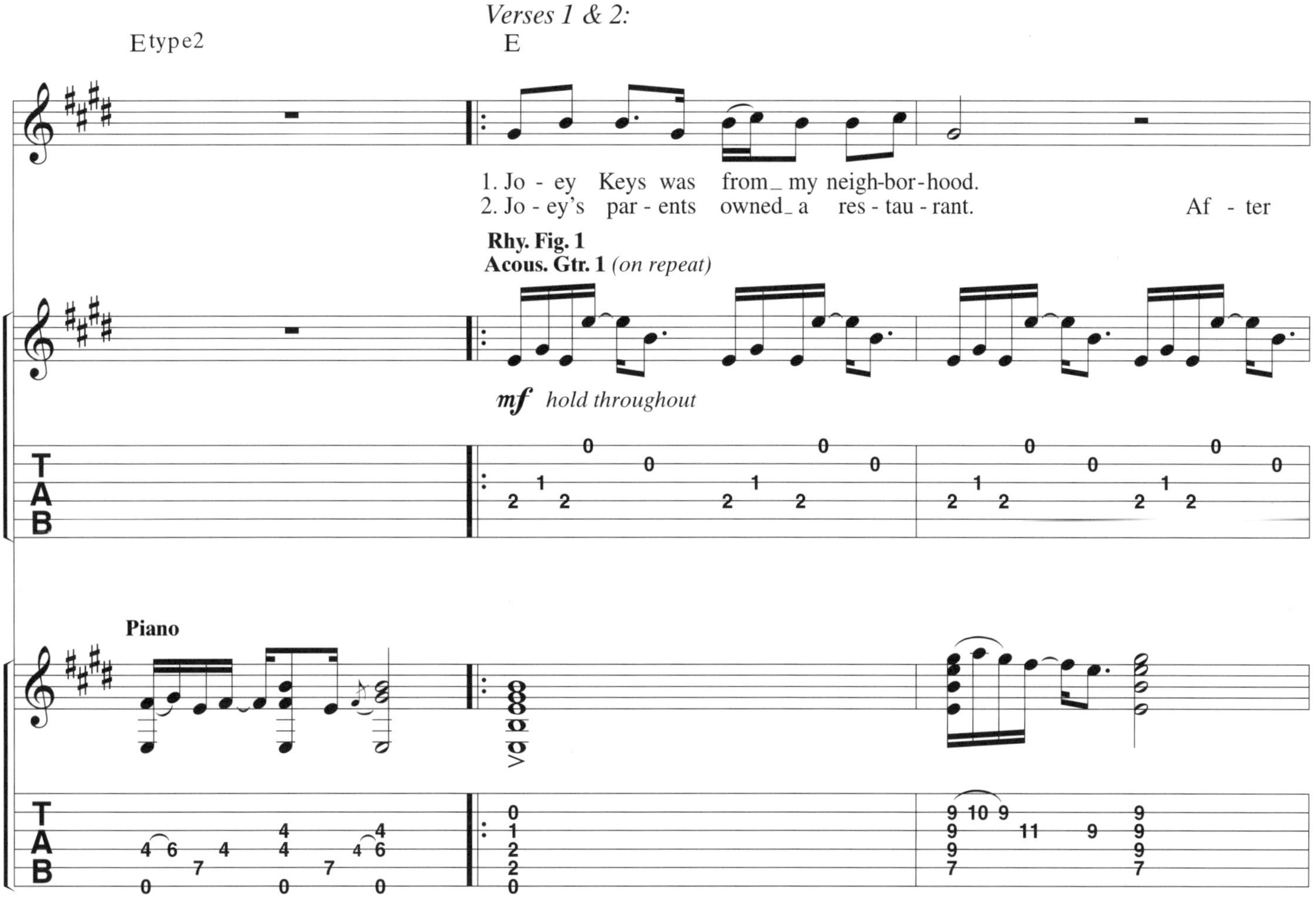

Etype2
Verses 1 & 2:
E
1. Jo - ey Keys was from_ my neigh-bor-hood.
2. Jo - ey's par - ents owned_ a res - tau - rant. Af - ter
Rhy. Fig. 1
Acous. Gtr. 1 (on repeat)
mf hold throughout
Piano

B C♯m

Some would say that he was bad, Joe thought that was good. They
clos - ing time they'd give us al - most an - y - thing we'd want. I

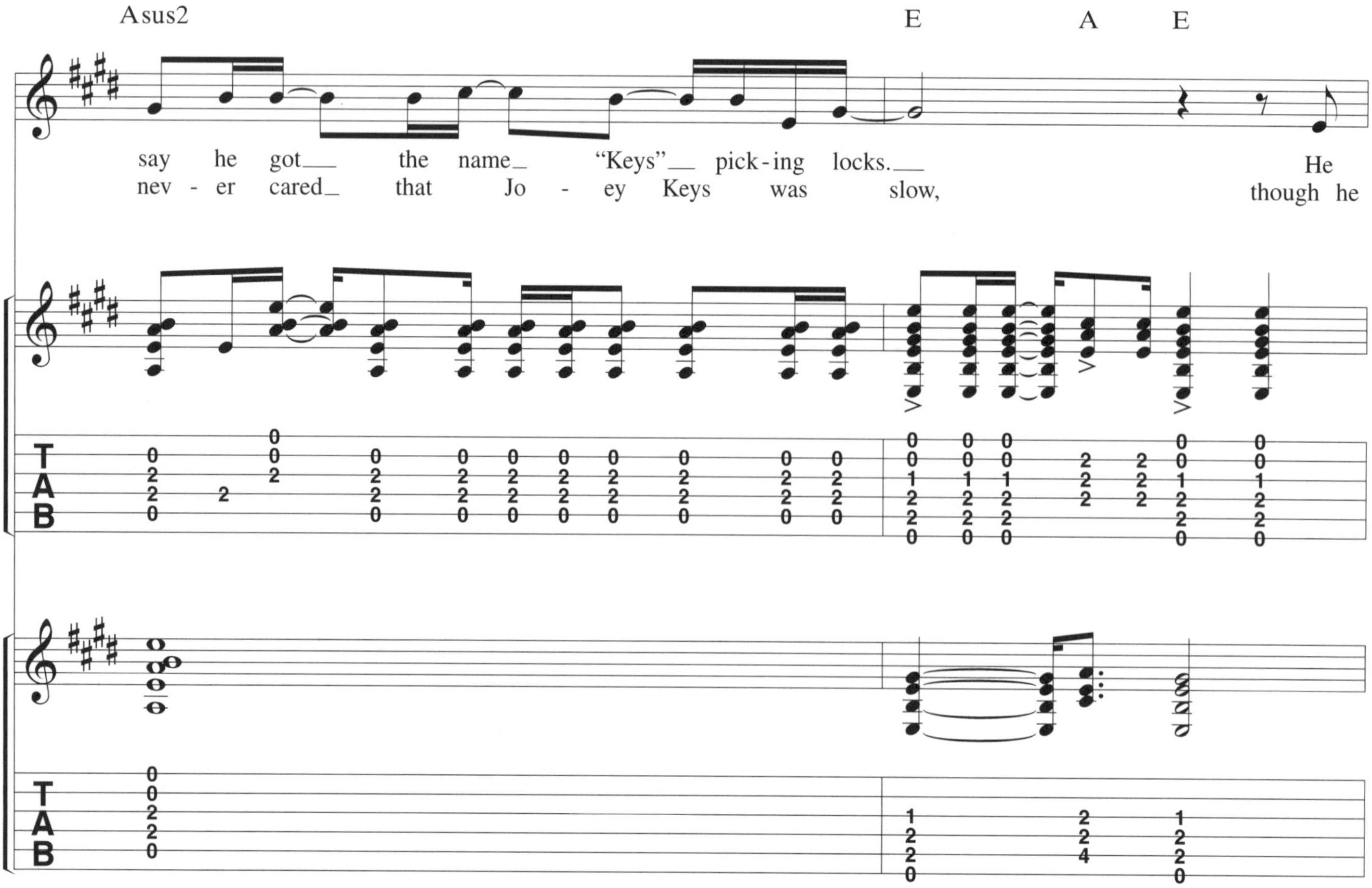

T A B

Asus2 E A E

say he got the name "Keys" pick - ing locks. He
nev - er cared that Jo - ey Keys was slow, though he

T A B

1.
F♯m7
G♯m7
Asus2
nev - er real - ly robbed no one; it sure a - mused_ the cops.
could - n't read or write too well,
2.
Asus2
E
Acous. Gtr. 1
we'd talk all_ night long.
Come on, come on, come on,_ what you gon-na
end Rhy. Fig. 1
Elec. Gtr. 1 (w/dist.)
mf

Asus2
F♯m(11)
Asus2
do__ with_ your life?_
Come on, come on, come on,__
chas-ing sparks
in the night._
His
E
Asus2
F♯m(11)
G♯m7(♯5)
old man said to-mor - row__is a
ride that goes_ no - where____ but I'll
pull some strings,_ get black-bird wings and
Chorus:
Asus
Bsus
C♯m7
Cont. rhy. simile
break us out of here.______
Hey,
Jo-ey,
come on and tell me 'bout_your dreams._Tell me all the

Asus2
F♯m(11)
B(11)/D♯
sights you're gon - na see. Tell me who you're gon - na be. Hey, Jo-ey, we're gon-na
C♯m7
F♯m(11)
G♯m7(♯5)
kiss the girls good - night. Some-times you got to stand and fight, it - 'll be all right,
To Coda
Asus2
Esus2
C♯sus2
we're gon-na find a bet-ter life. See,
Piano
hold throughout

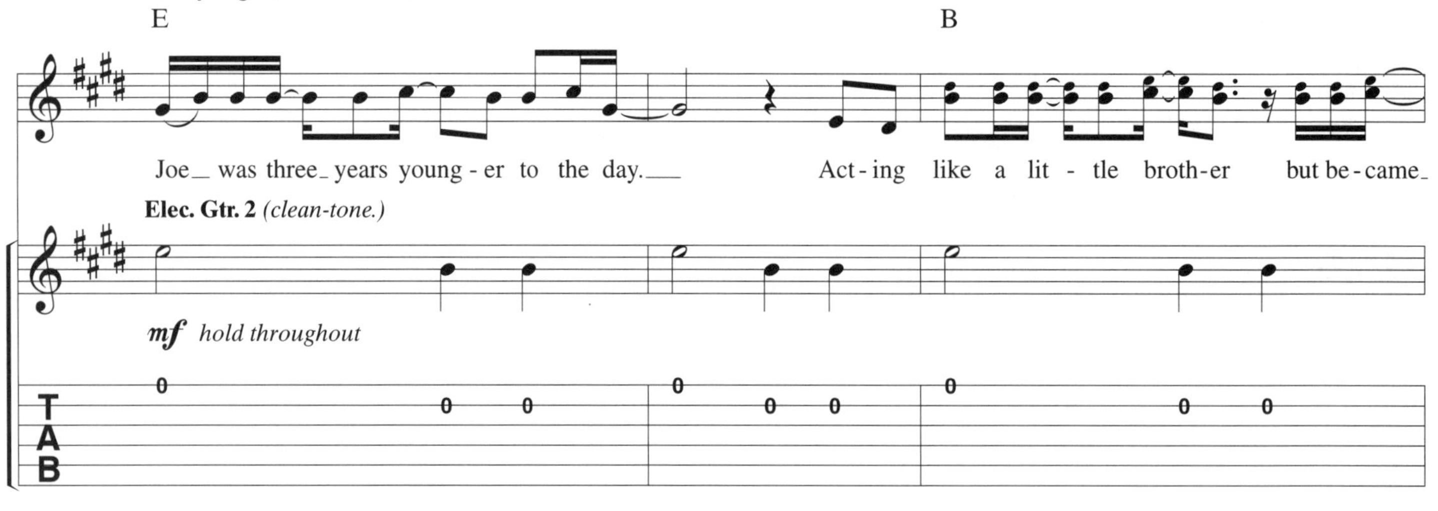

Verse 3:
w/Rhy. Fig.1 (Acous. Gtr. 1) simile
E
B
Joe was three years young - er to the day. Act - ing like a lit - tle broth - er but be - came
Elec. Gtr. 2 (clean-tone.)
mf hold throughout

C♯m
Asus2
E A E
my ball and chain. I met this girl named Rhon - da, she fell for me. She said,

F♯m7
G♯m7
Asus2
Chorus:
Bsus
Acous. Gtr. 1
"I might learn to like him but love ain't built for three." Hey, Jo-ey, come on and
Elec. Gtr. 1

C♯m7
Cont. rhy. simile
Asus2
F♯m(11)
tell me 'bout your dreams. Tell me all the sights you're gon - na see, tell me who you're gon - na be.
Bkgd. Vcl.: Who you gon-na be?
Elec. Gtr. 1
B(11)/D♯
C♯m7
Hey, Jo - ey, you're gon - na kiss the girls good - night. Some-times you got to
F♯m(11)
G♯m7(♯5)
Asus2
Guitar Solo:
Bsus
Acous. Gtr. 1
stand and fight, it'll be all right. Hey, Jo - ey.
Elec. Gtr. 3 (w/dist.)
mf
Elec. Gtr. 1

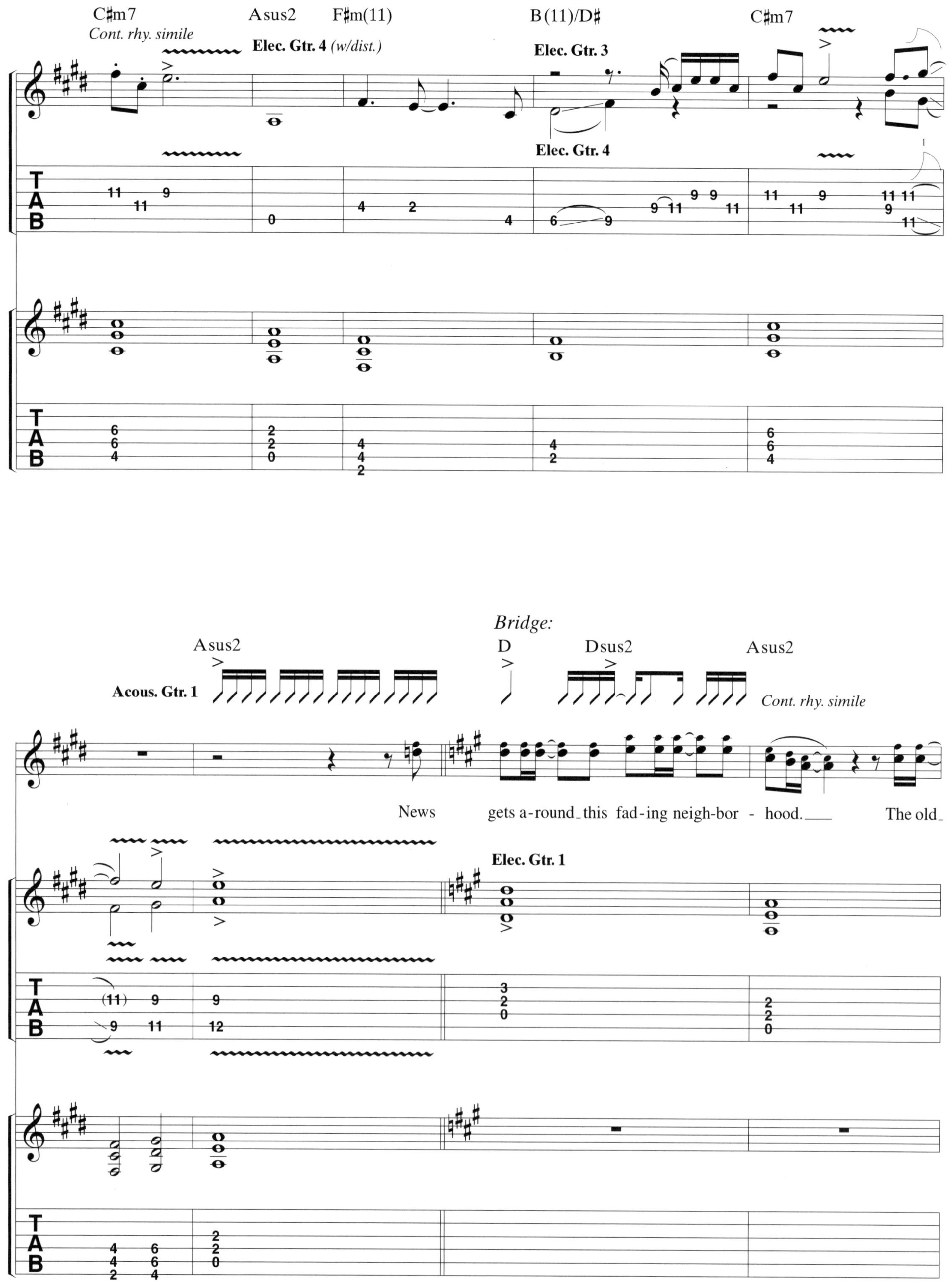

Bridge:

Asus2 D Dsus2 Asus2

Acous. Gtr. 1 *Cont. rhy. simile*

News gets a-round this fad-ing neigh-bor - hood. The old

Elec. Gtr. 1

E
D
Dsus2
man lost the res - tau-rant, he drinks more than he should. It's time for Jo-ey Keys to do some
Asus2
F♯m(11)
G♯m7(♯5)
Asus2
D.S. al Coda
good. Pick the lock off our lives, let's get out of here, like we al-ways said we would.
Coda
E
Acous. Gtr. 1
Asus2
E
Asus2
Cont. rhy. simile
life. Find a bet-ter life, find a bet-ter
Elec. Gtr. 1
E
Asus2
F♯m(11)
Bsus
life. Uh, huh, uh, huh.

Outro:
E Vocals tacet on repeat
Asus2
Cont. rhy. simile
Come on, come on, come on, what you gon-na do with your life? Come on,
F♯m(11)
Bsus
E/G♯*
come on, come on, come on, chas-ing sparks in the nights. Tell the old man it's to-mor-row; we're off
*Played by Bass gtr. only.
Asus2
1.
F♯m(11)
to find some-where. Well, I pulled those strings, got black-bird wings that
Bsus
2.
F♯m(11)
G♯m7(♯5)
Bsus
Repeat and fade
got us out of here.

MISUNDERSTOOD

Words and Music by
JON BON JOVI, RICHIE SAMBORA,
ANDREAS CARLSSON and DESMOND CHILD

G5/F♯ Em7 Dsus

I___ died, I should have shut_ my mouth, things head - ed south.
I___ tried to stretch the truth_ but did - n't lie.

1.

C(2) G/B Asus

As the words slipped off_ my tongue, they sound - ed dumb._ If this old heart could talk_

Elec. Gtr. 2 *(w/dist.)*

mf

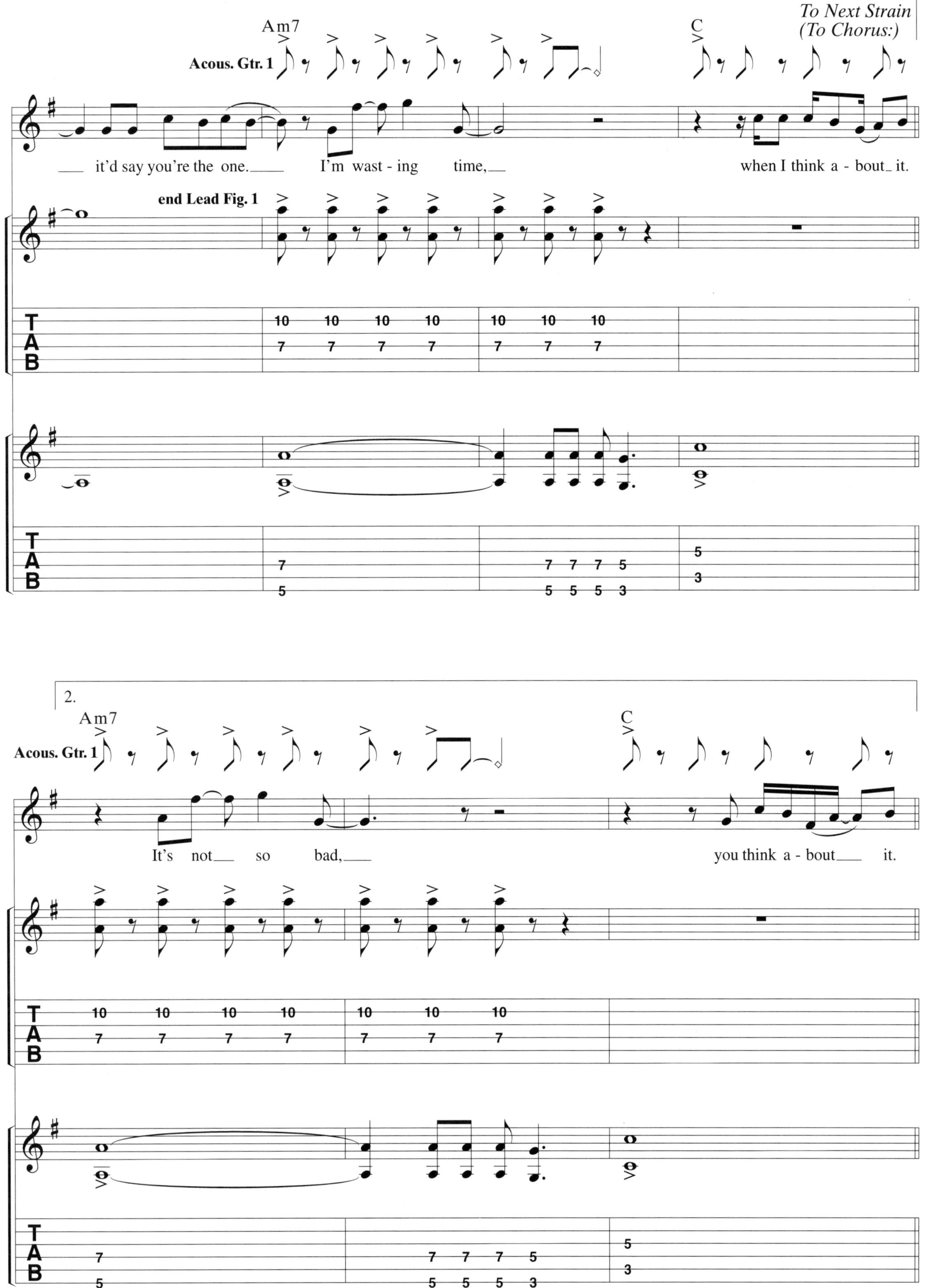
To Next Strain
(To Chorus:)
Am7
C
Acous. Gtr. 1
it'd say you're the one. I'm wast - ing time, when I think a - bout it.
end Lead Fig. 1
T
A
B
10 10 10 10 10 10 10
7 7 7 7 7 7 7
7 7 7 7 5
5 5 5 5 3
5
3
2.
Am7
C
Acous. Gtr. 1
It's not so bad, you think a - bout it.
10 10 10 10 10 10 10
7 7 7 7 7 7 7
7 7 7 7 5
5 5 5 5 3
5
3

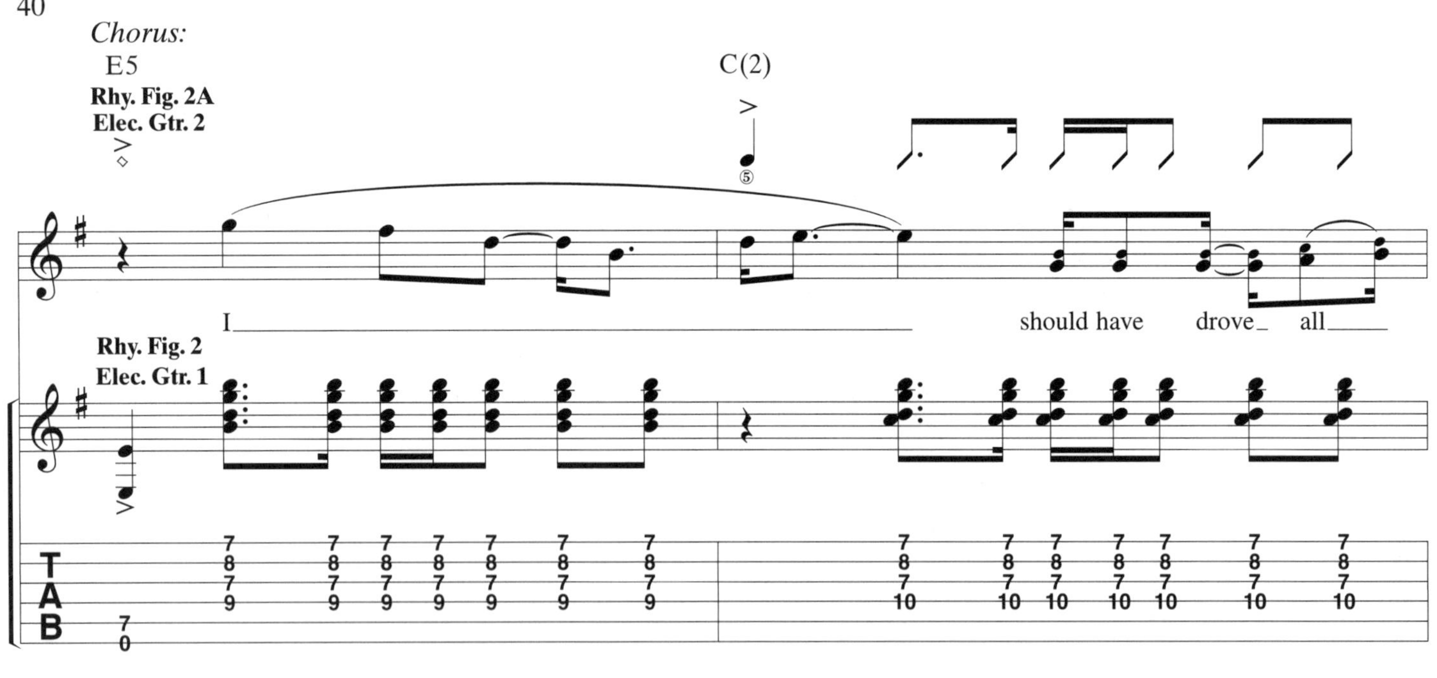
Chorus:
E5
C(2)
Rhy. Fig. 2A
Elec. Gtr. 2
I ___ should have drove_ all___
Rhy. Fig. 2
Elec. Gtr. 1
TAB

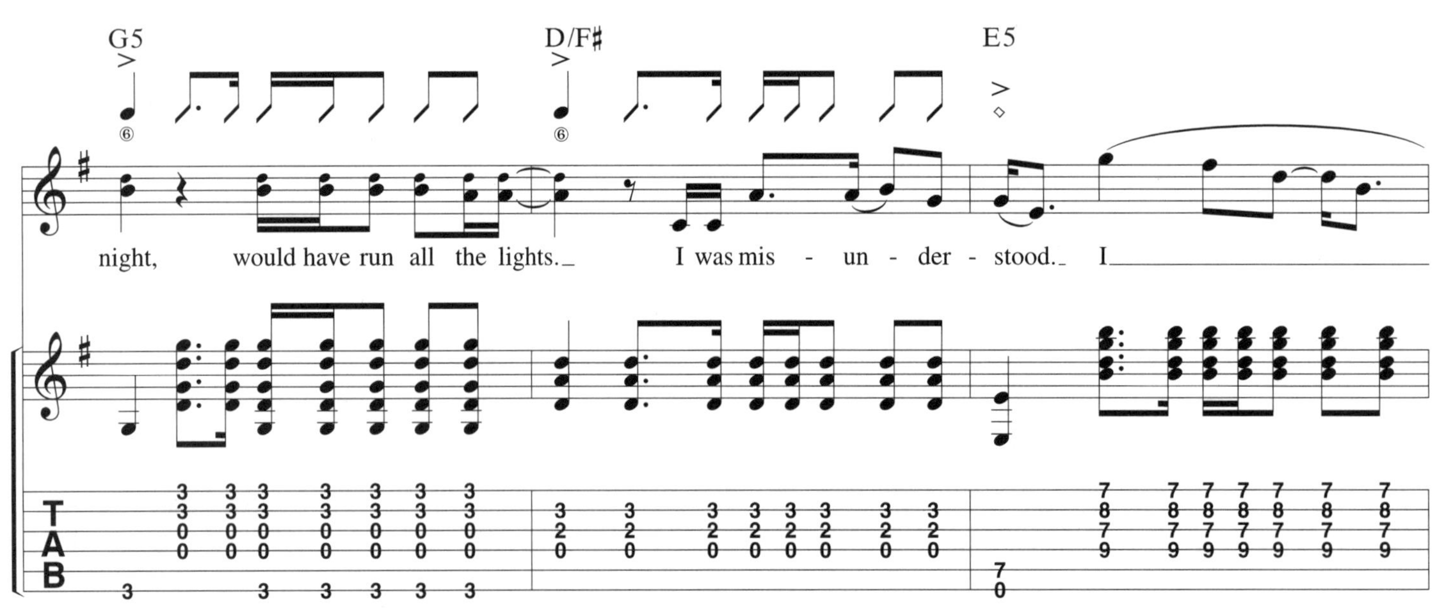
G5
D/F#
E5
night, would have run all the lights._ I was mis - un - der - stood._ I___
TAB

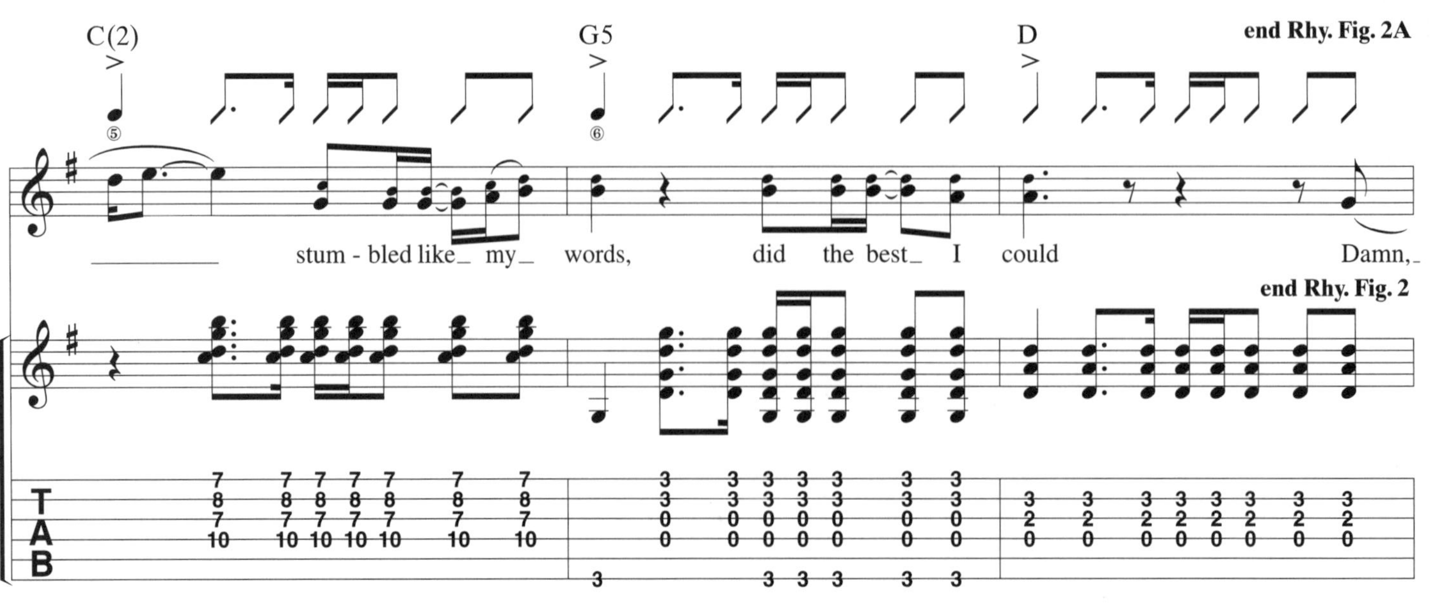
C(2)
G5
D
end Rhy. Fig. 2A
___ stum - bled like_ my_ words, did the best_ I could Damn,_
end Rhy. Fig. 2
TAB

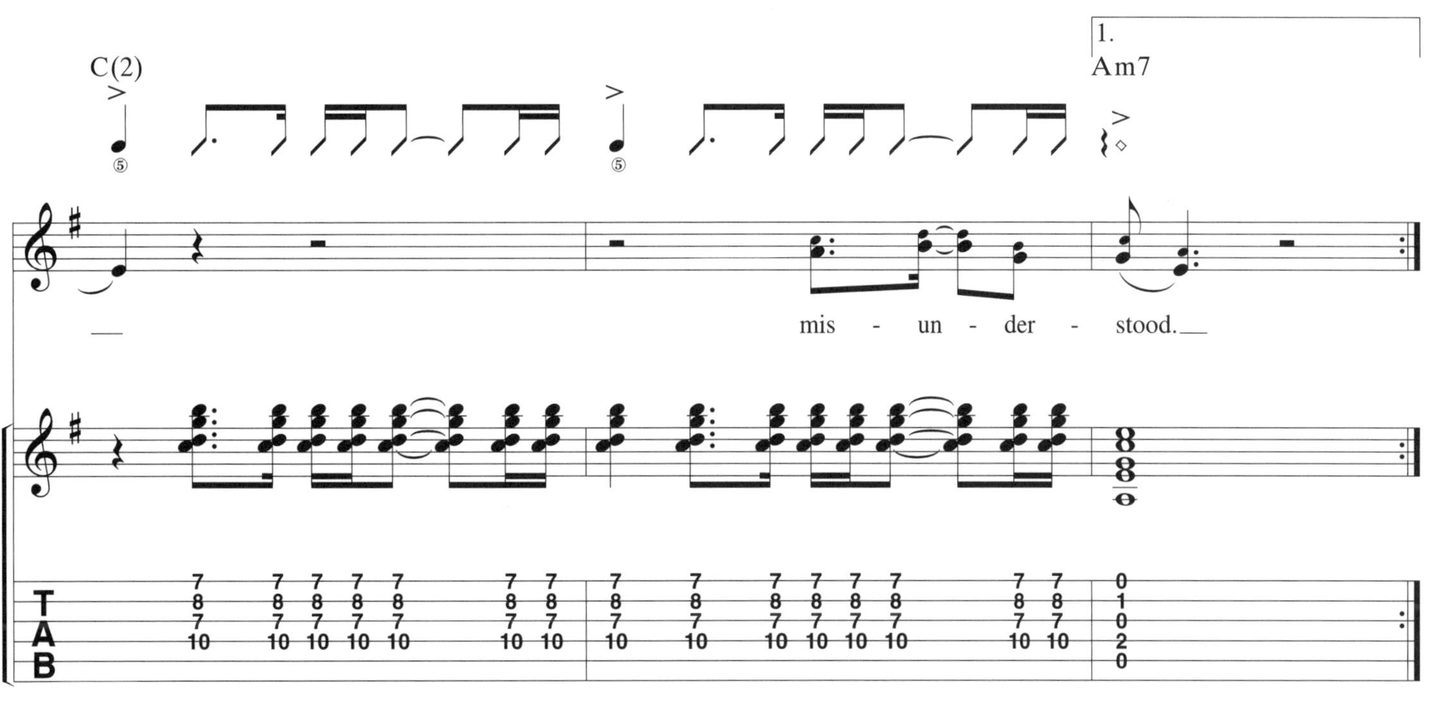
C(2)
1.
Am7
mis - un - der - stood.

Guitar Solo:
w/Rhy. Fig. 1 (Elec. Gtrs. 1 & 2 & Acous. Gtr. 1) simile
2.
A5
Am
Cmaj9
G5
stood.
In - ten - tions
good.
Elec. Gtr. 3 (w/dist.)

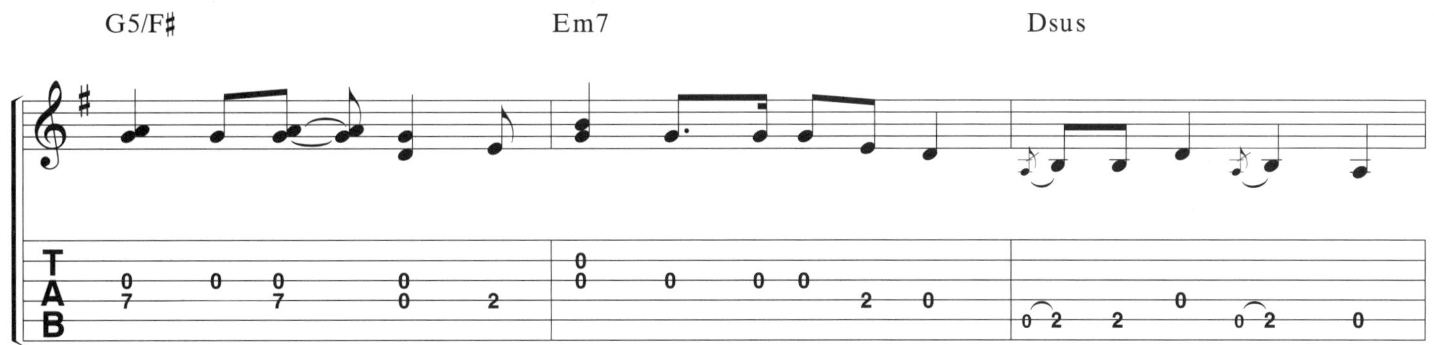
G5/F♯
Em7
Dsus

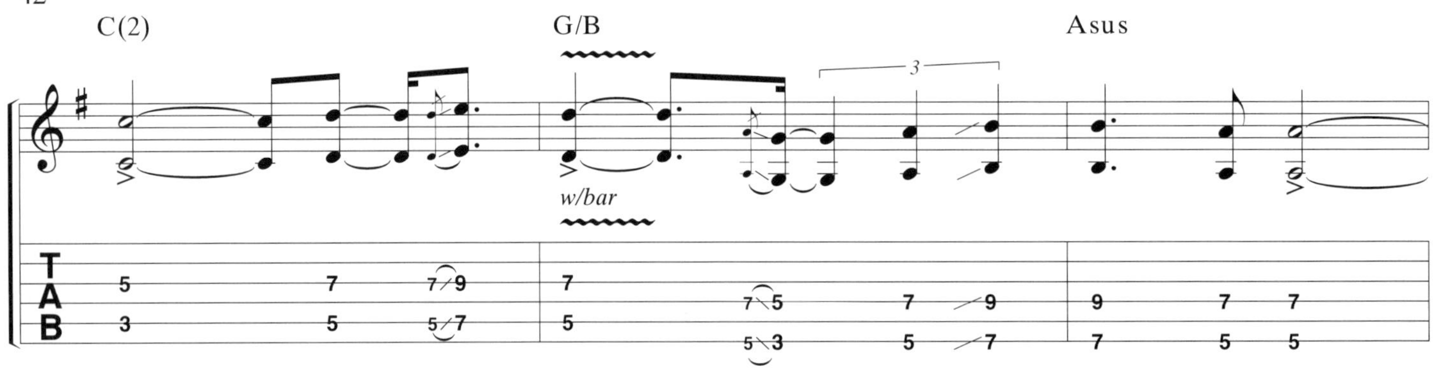

Am7 C

Acous. Gtr. 1

It's you_ and I,__ just think a - bout__ it...

Elec. Gtr. 3

Elec. Gtr. 1

Outro Chorus:

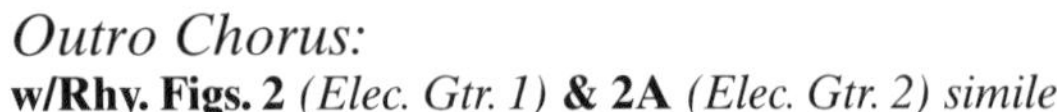
w/Rhy. Figs. 2 *(Elec. Gtr. 1)* **& 2A** *(Elec. Gtr. 2) simile*

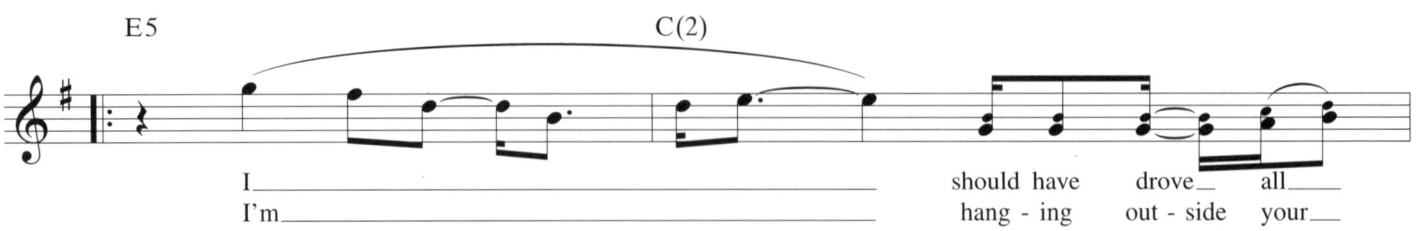

1.
C(2)
G5
D
stum-bled like_ my_ words, did the best_ I could.
stum-bled like_ my_ words, did the best_ I

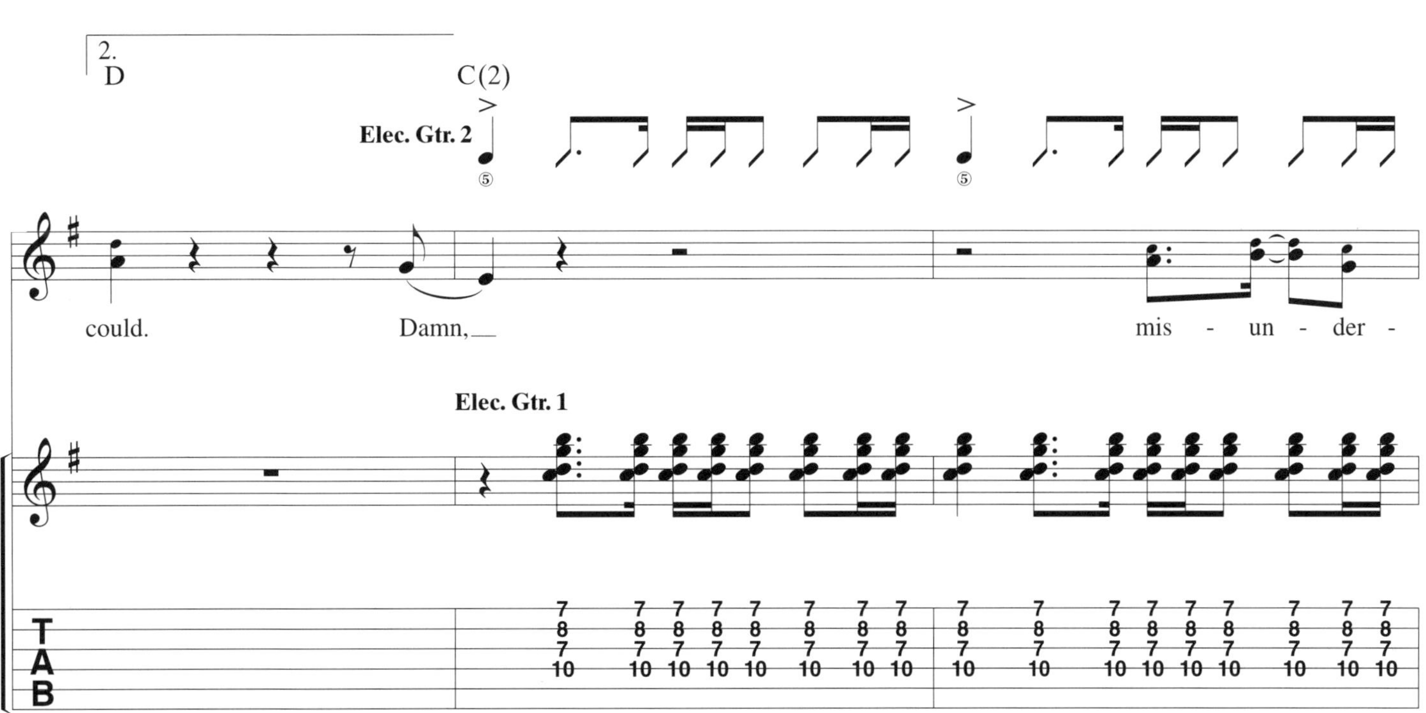
2.
D
C(2)
Elec. Gtr. 2
could. Damn,_ mis - un - der -
Elec. Gtr. 1

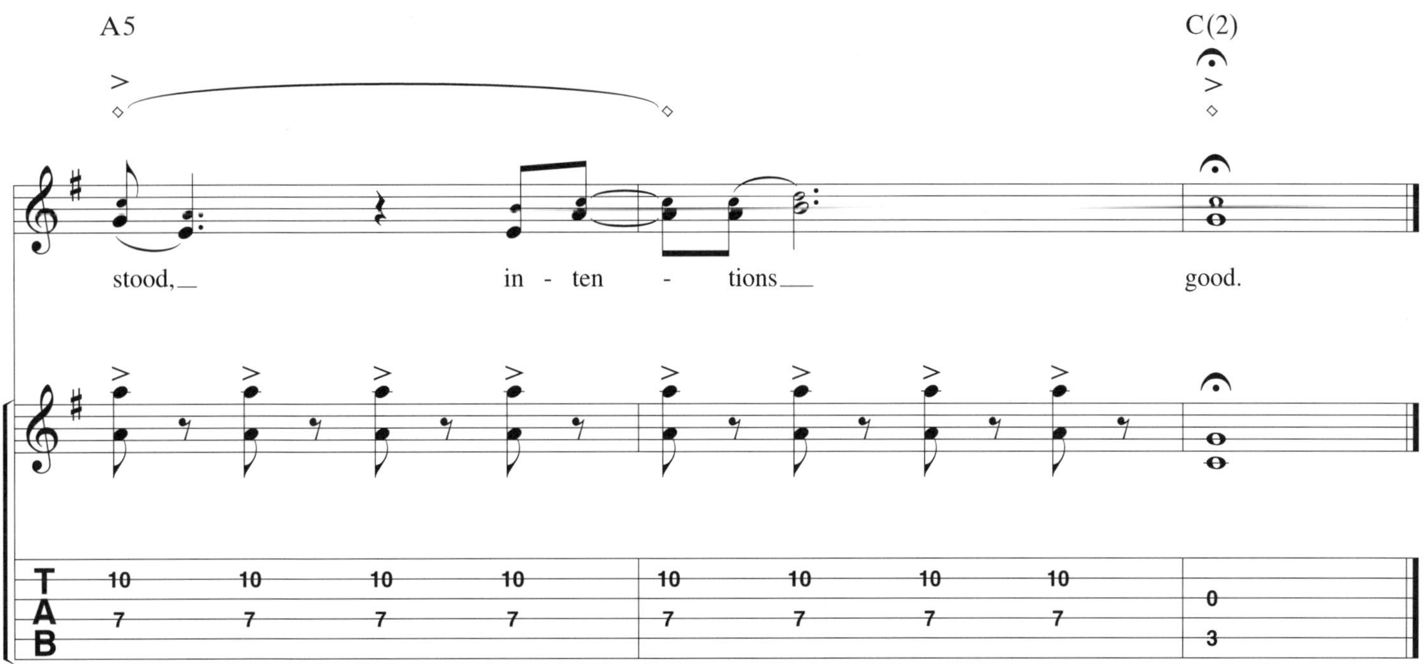
A5
C(2)
stood,_ in - ten - tions_ good.

ALL ABOUT LOVIN' YOU

Words and Music by
JON BON JOVI, RICHIE SAMBORA,
ANDREAS CARLSSON and DESMOND CHILD

F6(9)
C(9)
mem-o-ries of me and you.
Mis-takes, you know I've made a few._ 1. I
w/Rhy. Fig. 1 (Acous. Gtr. 1) simile
w/Lead Fig. 1 (Elec. Gtr. 3) 4 times on repeat
G5
D(11)/F♯
F6(9)
took some shots_ and fell_ from time ___ to time,_ ba-by, you were there to pull me through_ We've
(2.) lived, I've loved,_ I've lost,_ I've paid some dues ba - by, we've been to hell and back a - gain.___
Elec. Gtr. 2 (clean-tone)
mf hold throughout
C(9)
Em7
C(9)
been a - round_ that block_ a time or two.___ I'm gon-na lay it on the line..
Through it all___ you're al - ways my best friend._ For all the words I did - n't say_
Lead Fig. 1
Elec. Gtr. 3 (clean-tone)
end Lead Fig. 1
w/flanger effect
Acous. Gtr. 1

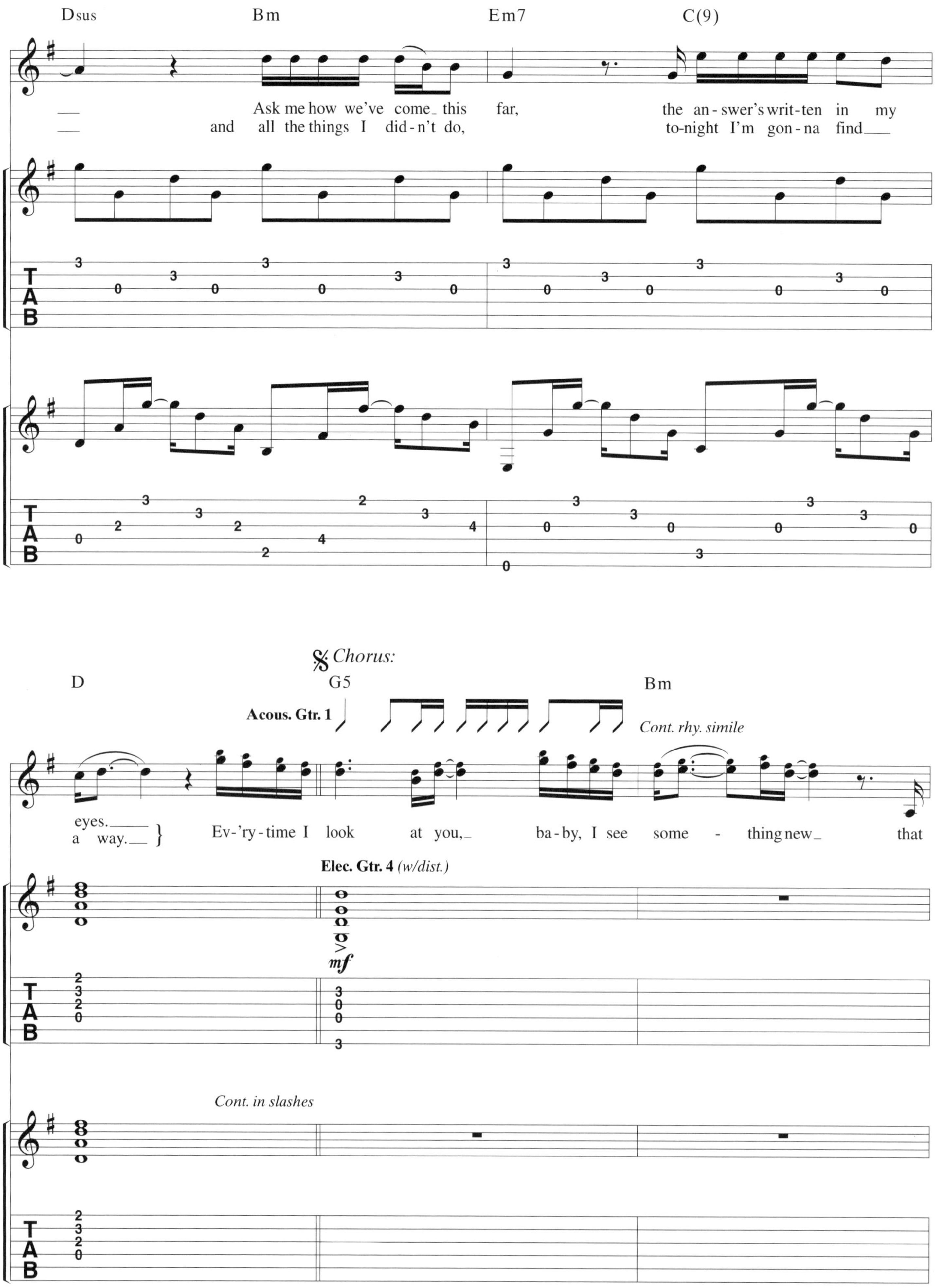

Dsus Bm Em7 C(9)

— Ask me how we've come this far, the an - swer's writ - ten in my
— and all the things I did - n't do, to-night I'm gon - na find —

D

𝄋 *Chorus:*

G5 Bm

Acous. Gtr. 1 *Cont. rhy. simile*

eyes. —
a way. — } Ev - 'ry - time I look at you, — ba - by, I see some - thing new — that

Elec. Gtr. 4 *(w/dist.)*

mf

Cont. in slashes

C
Cm
G5
takes me high - er than_ be-fore_ and makes me want_ you more._ I don't wan-na sleep to-night,_dream-in's just a
Bm
Em
F
To Coda
1.
D
C(9)
Acous. Gtr. 1
waste of time._ When I look at what_ my life's_been com-in' to, I'm all a-bout lov-in' you._
2.
D
C(9)
Bridge:
Am
G/B
Acous. Gtr. 1
2. I've to, I'm all a-bout lov-in' you. You can take_ this world_ a - way,_

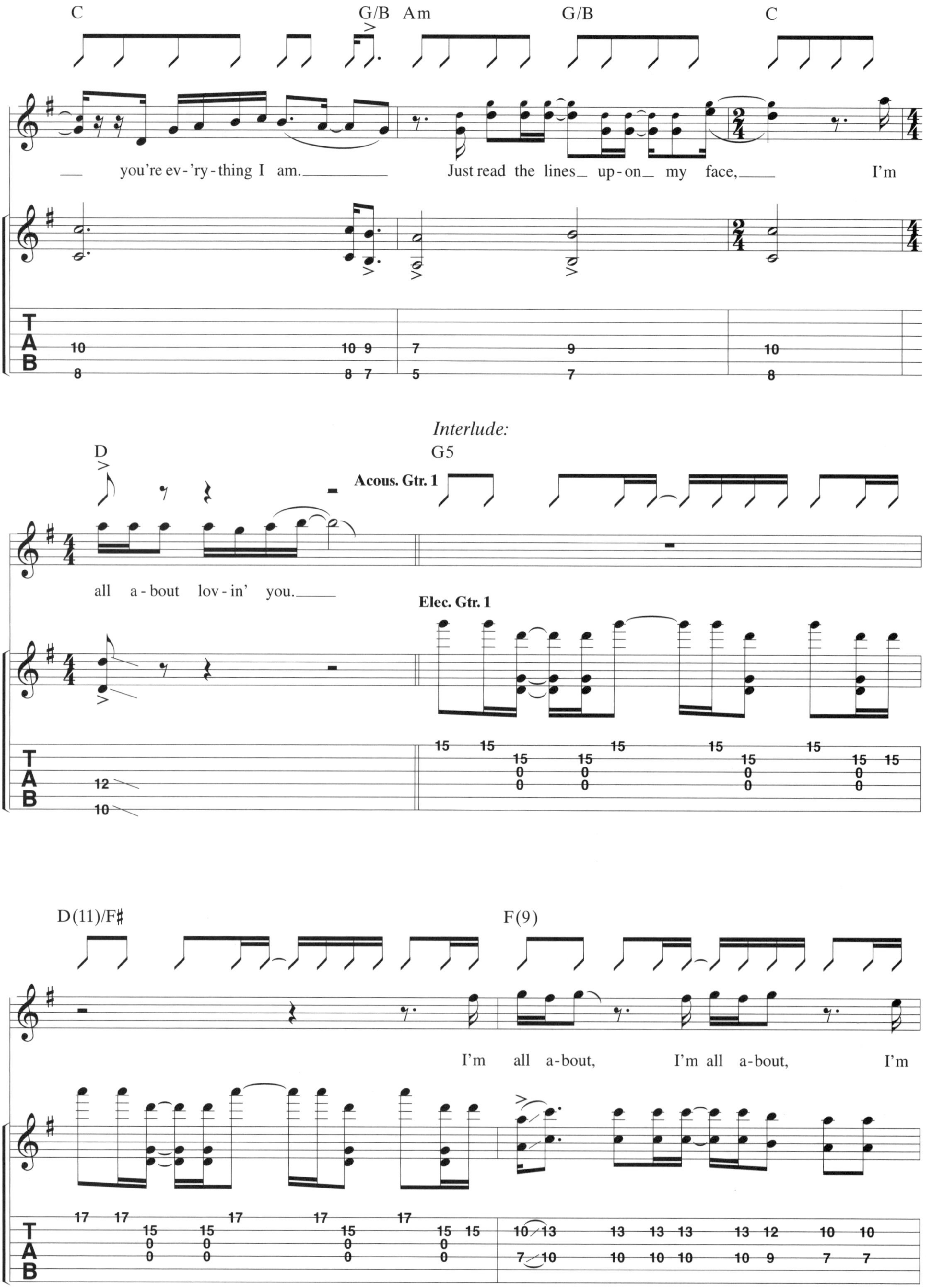

C G/B Am G/B C

you're ev-'ry-thing I am. Just read the lines upon my face, I'm

D

Interlude:

G5

Acous. Gtr. 1

all a-bout lov-in' you.

Elec. Gtr. 1

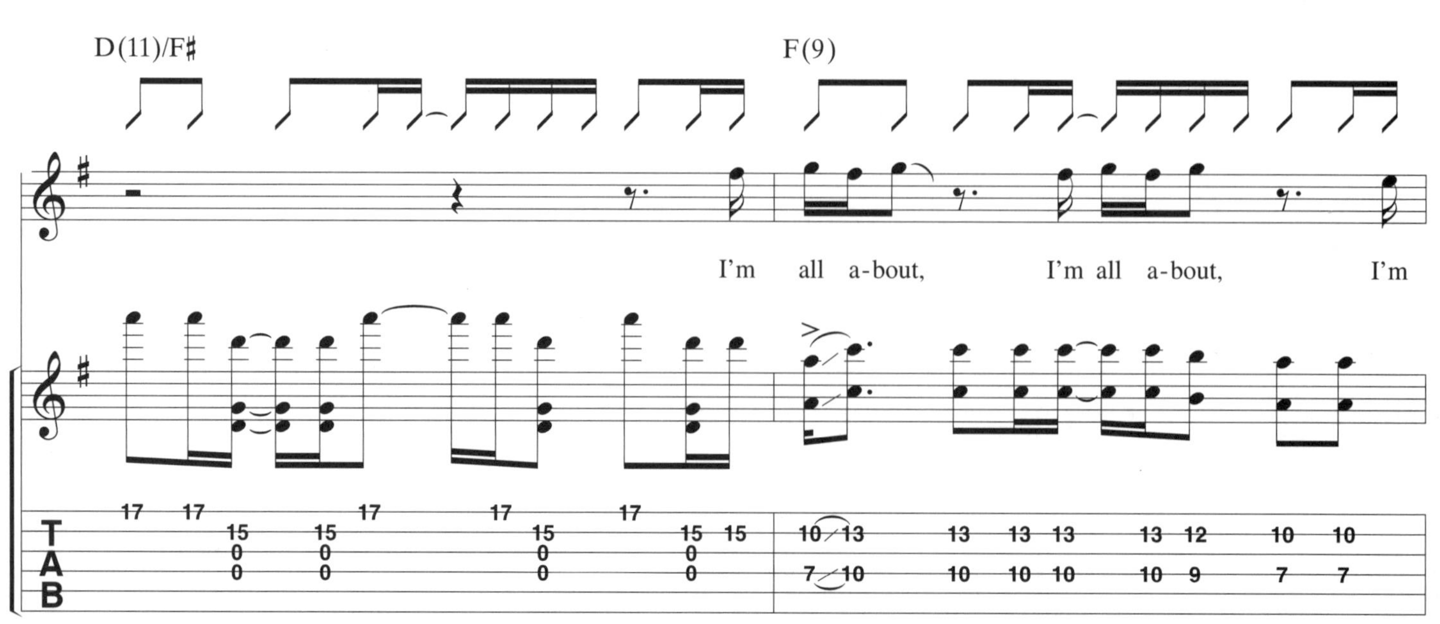

C
D.S. al Coda
D
C(9)
Acous. Gtr. 1 & Elec. Gtr. 4
Coda
all a-bout lov-in' you. Ev-'ry-time I
do, I'm all a-bout lov-in' you.

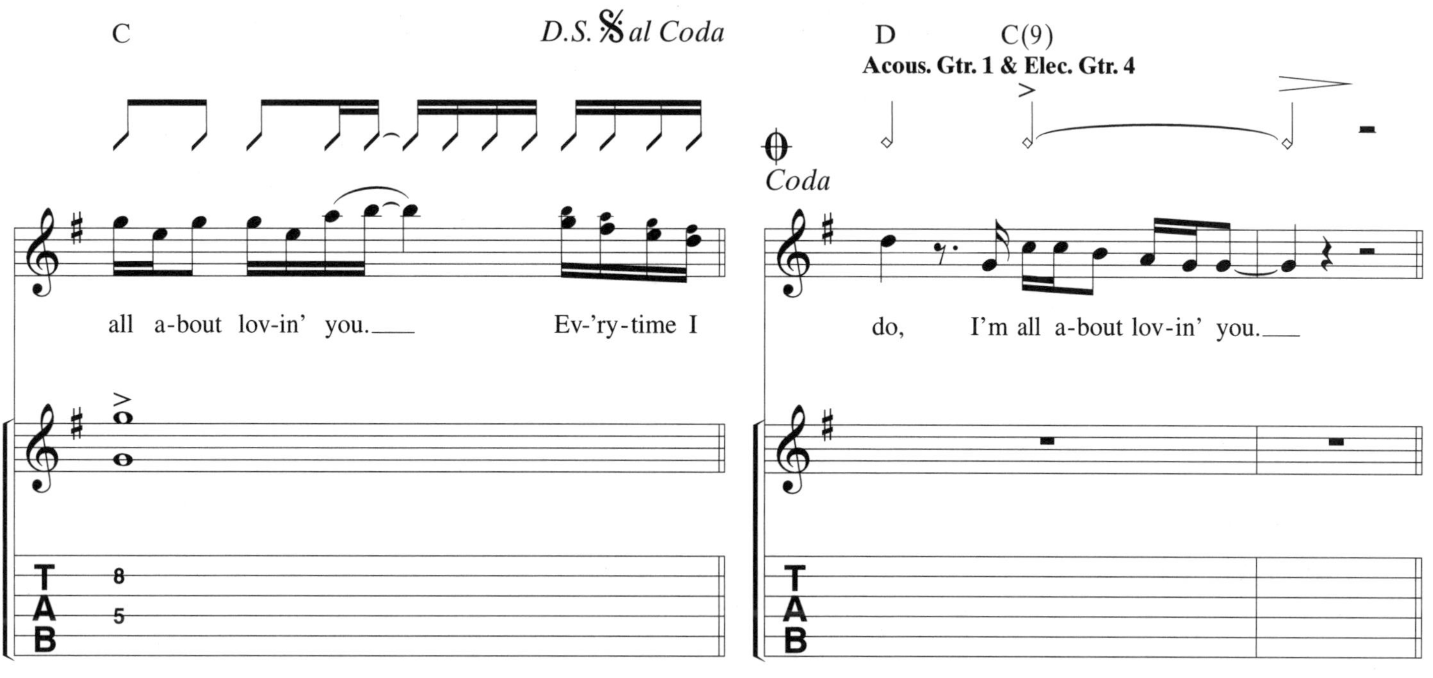

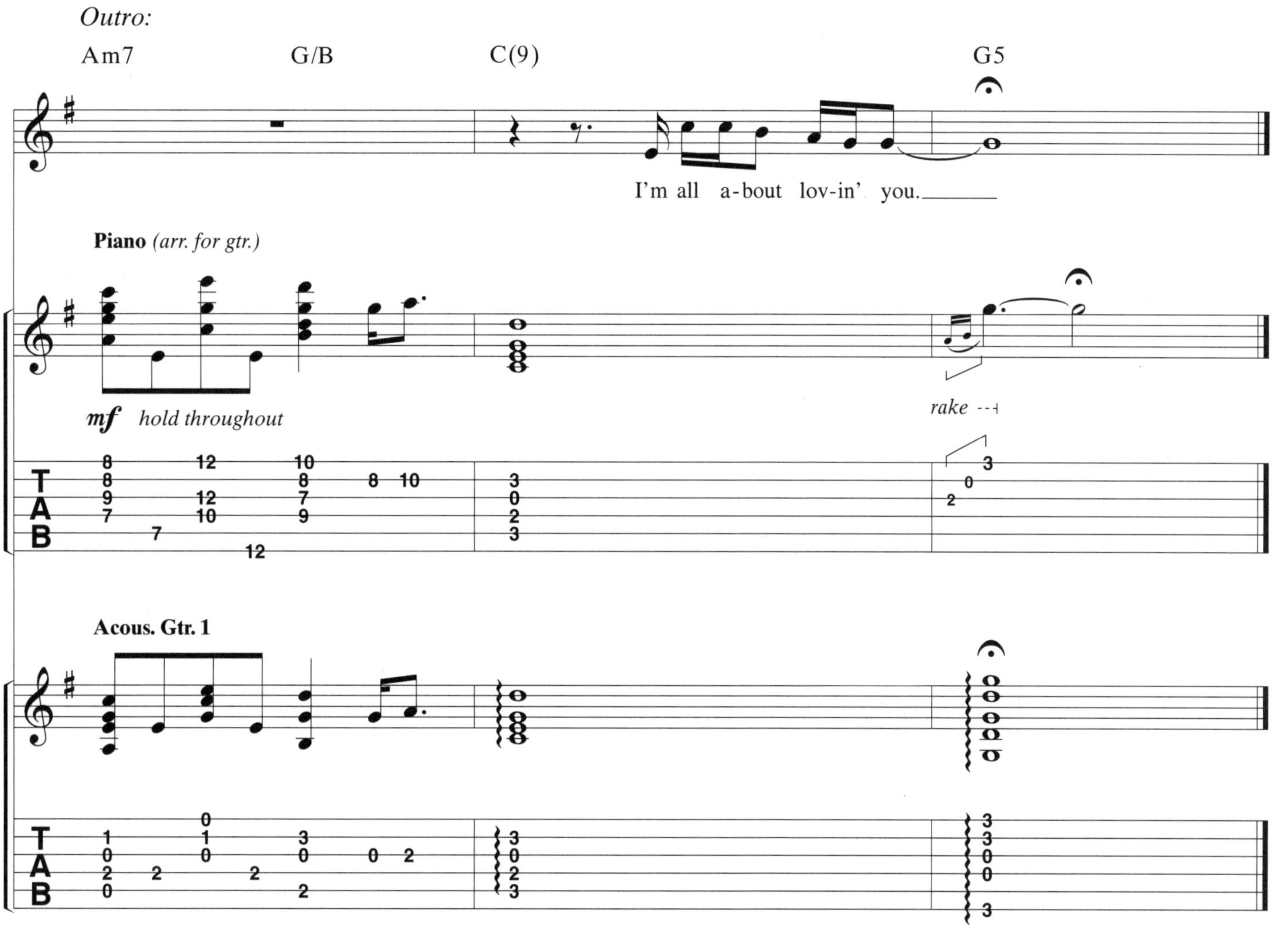

Outro:
Am7
G/B
C(9)
G5
I'm all a-bout lov-in' you.
Piano (arr. for gtr.)
mf hold throughout
rake
Acous. Gtr. 1

HOOK ME UP

Words and Music by
JON BON JOVI, RICHIE SAMBORA,
ANDREAS CARLSSON and DESMOND CHILD

All gtrs. w/Drop D tuning: ⑥ = D

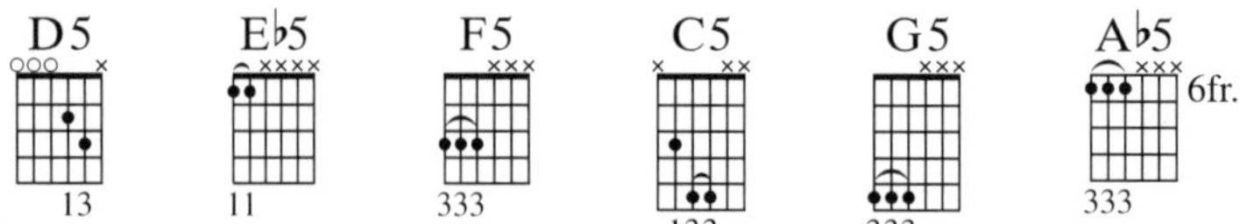

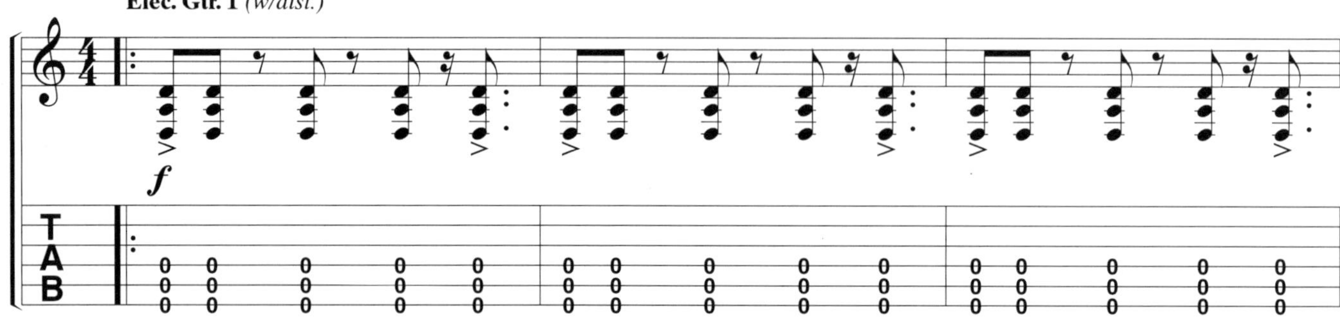

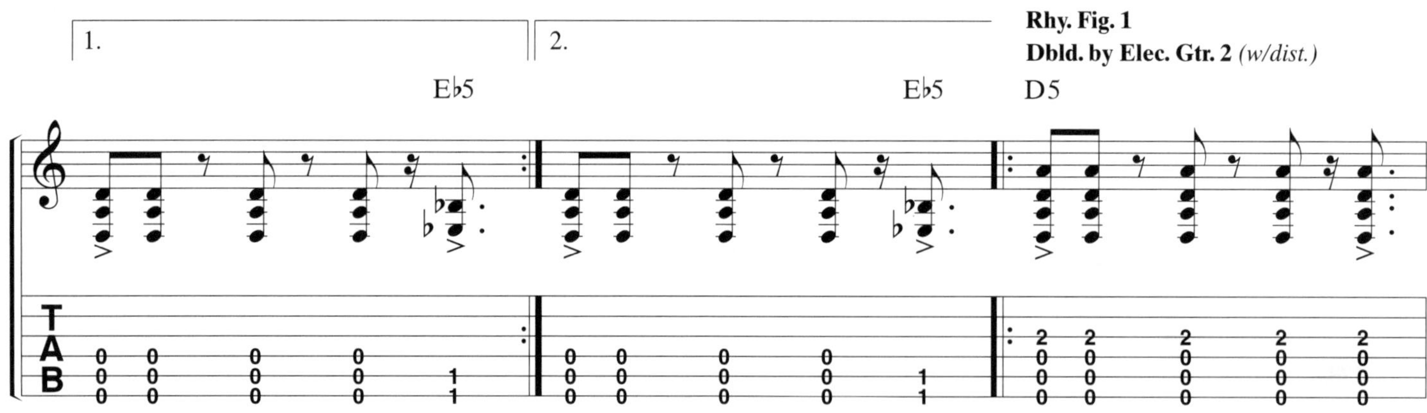

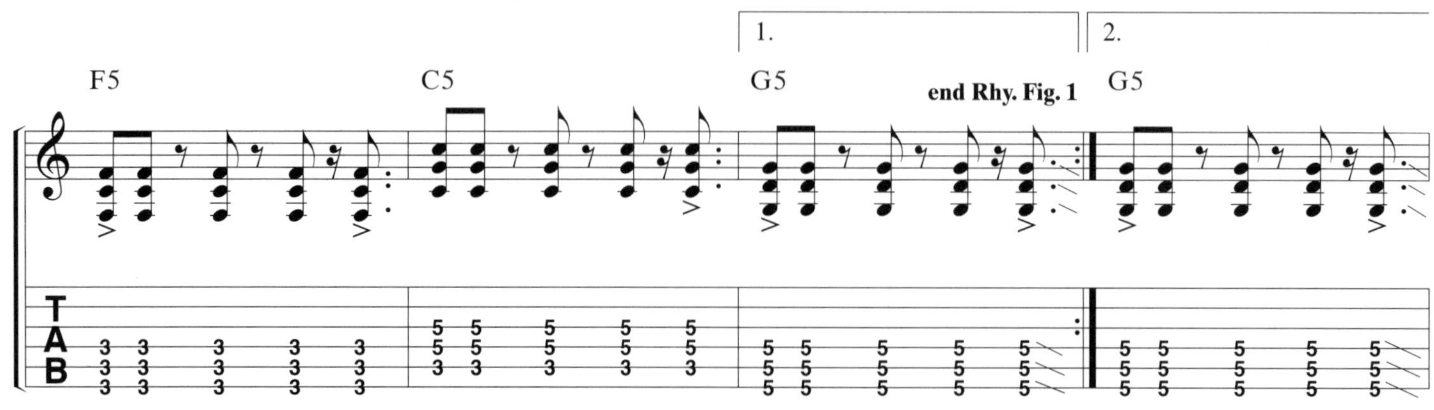

D5
1. Hel - lo,
Lead Fig. 1
Bass (arr. for gtr.)
end Lead Fig. 1
mf
Verse:
w/Lead Fig. 1 (Bass) 2 times, simile
N.C.
is there an - y - bod - y out there?
I'm a - lone,
Tell me what you're feel - ing,
your fears
w/Rhy. Fig. 1 (Elec. Gtr. 1) 2 3/4 times, simile
D5
F5
C5
G5
hang - ing by a thread.
Ev -
and all your wild - est dreams.
Ev -
D5
F5
C5
- 'ry - where a - round the world
ev - 'ry - bod - y's wait - ing for some -
- 'ry - one a - round the world
is feel - ing just the same way that we
G5
D5
F5
- day.
Call - ing out a - round the world.
are.
Reach - ing out a - round the world.
Will

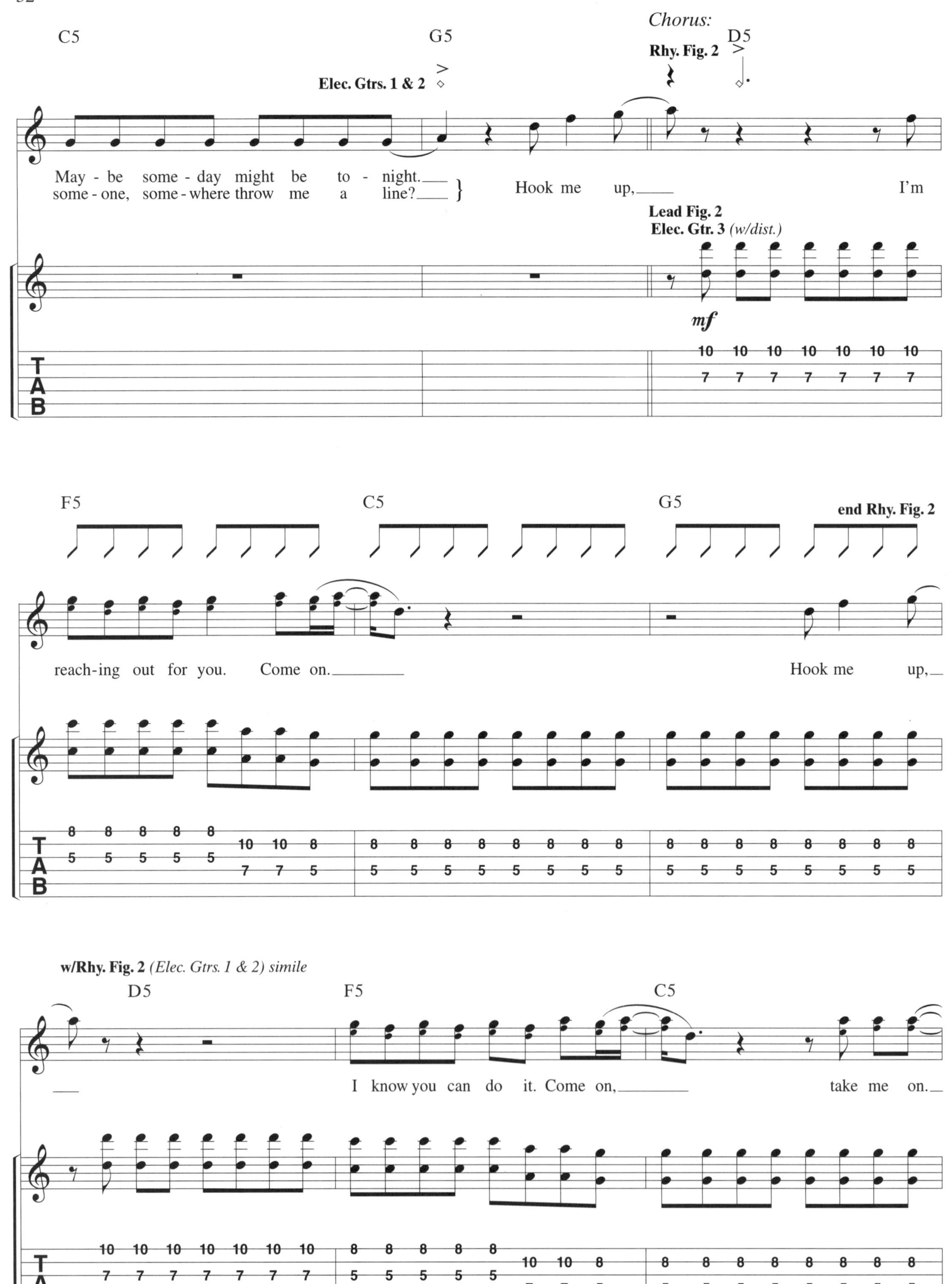
Chorus:
C5
G5
D5
Rhy. Fig. 2
Elec. Gtrs. 1 & 2
May - be some - day might be to - night.
some - one, some - where throw me a line?
Hook me up,
I'm
Lead Fig. 2
Elec. Gtr. 3 (w/dist.)
mf
F5
C5
G5
end Rhy. Fig. 2
reach-ing out for you. Come on.
Hook me up,
w/Rhy. Fig. 2 (Elec. Gtrs. 1 & 2) simile
D5
F5
C5
I know you can do it. Come on,
take me on.

1.
2.
w/Lead Fig. 2 (Elec. Gtr. 3) 1st 7 meas., simile
G5
G5
D5
F5
Elec. Gtrs. 1 & 2
2. Are you there?
Save
me,
end Lead Fig. 2
C5
G5
D5
F5
save
me.
Save
me,
C5
G5
A♭5
G5
save
me.
Elec. Gtr. 3
w/Lead Fig. 1 (Bass) 1st 2 meas., simile
D5 E♭5
D5
Hel - lo,
is there an - y - bod - y out there?

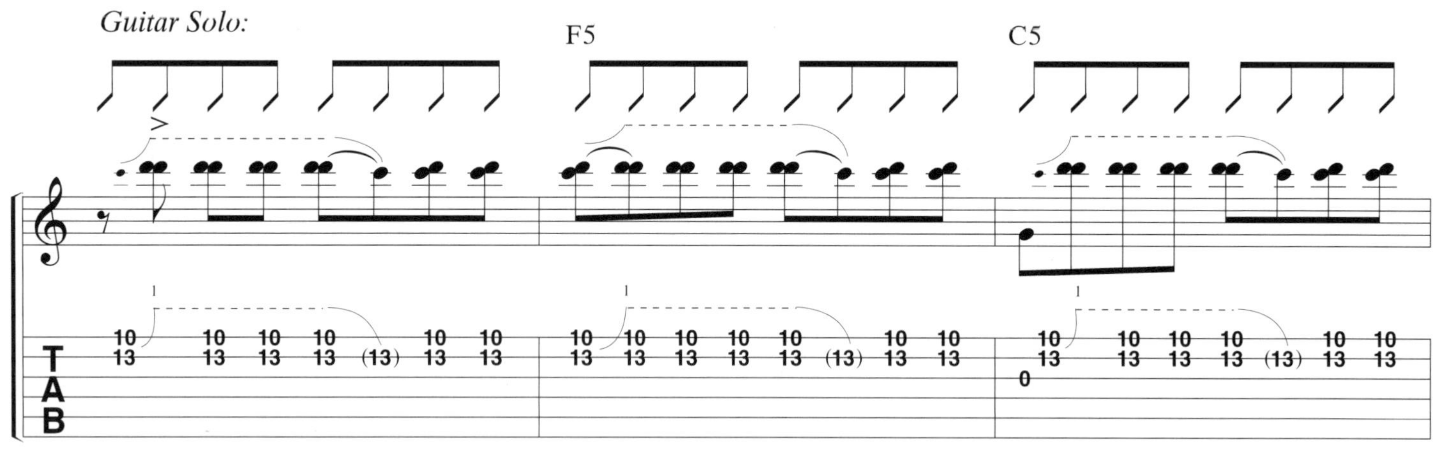
Guitar Solo:
F5
C5

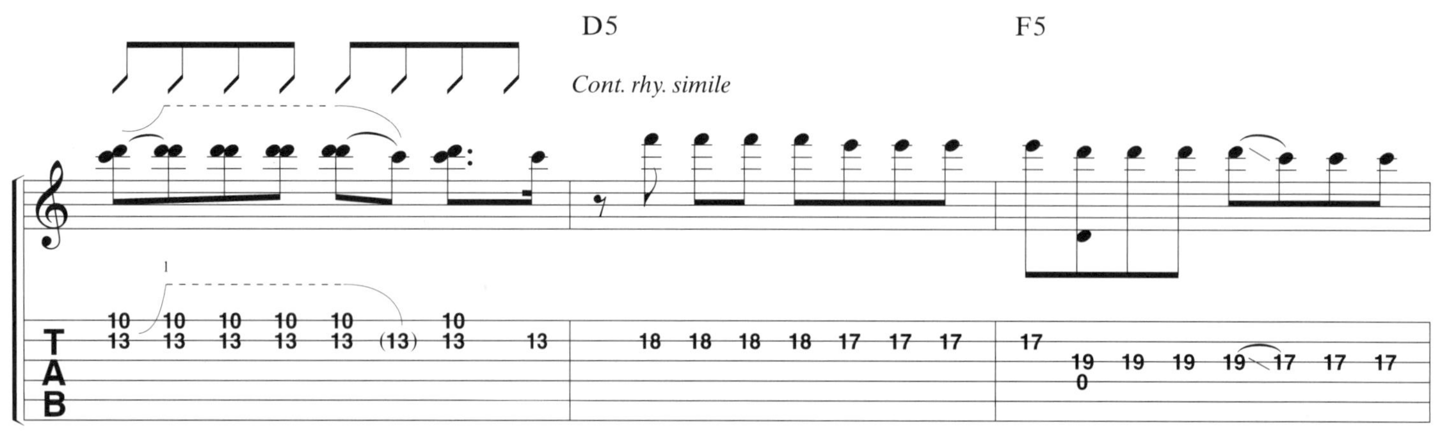
D5
Cont. rhy. simile
F5

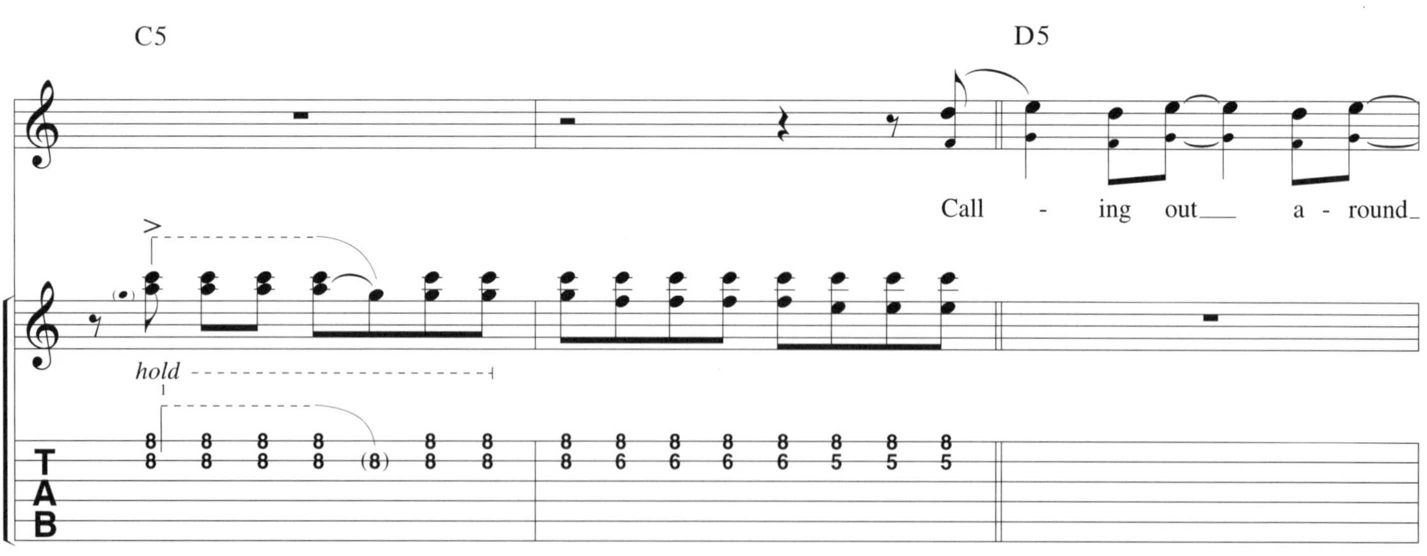
C5
D5
Call - ing out a - round
hold

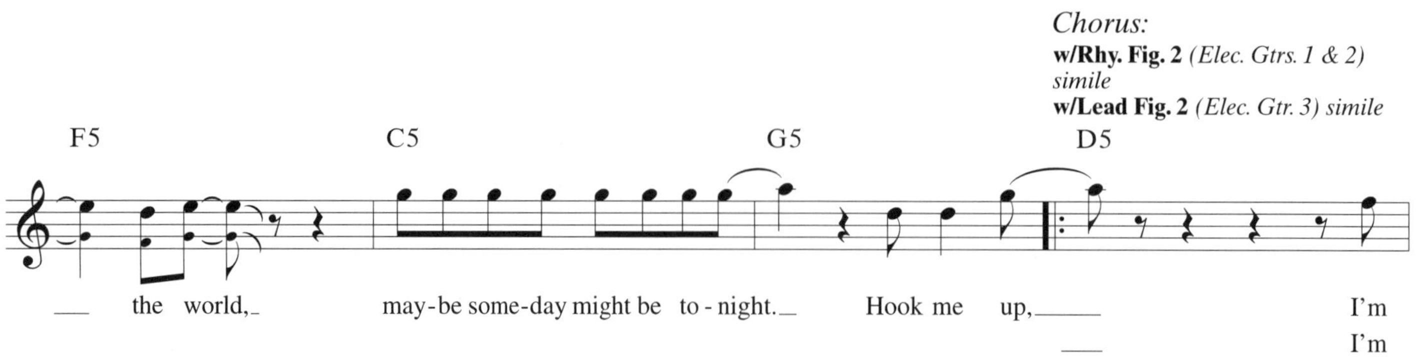
Chorus:
w/Rhy. Fig. 2 (Elec. Gtrs. 1 & 2) simile
w/Lead Fig. 2 (Elec. Gtr. 3) simile
F5
C5
G5
D5
the world, may-be some-day might be to-night. Hook me up, I'm
I'm

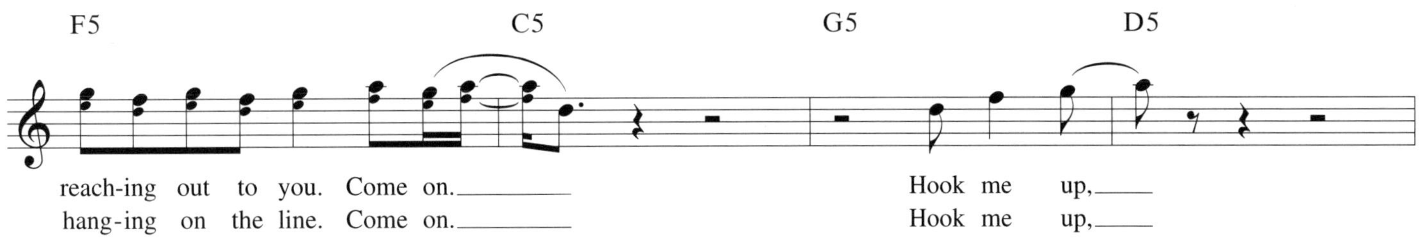
F5
C5
G5
D5
reach-ing out to you. Come on.
hang-ing on the line. Come on.
Hook me up,
Hook me up,

1.
2.
F5
C5
G5
G5
I know you can do it. Come on,
make me come a-live. Come on,
take me on.
take me on.
Hook me up,

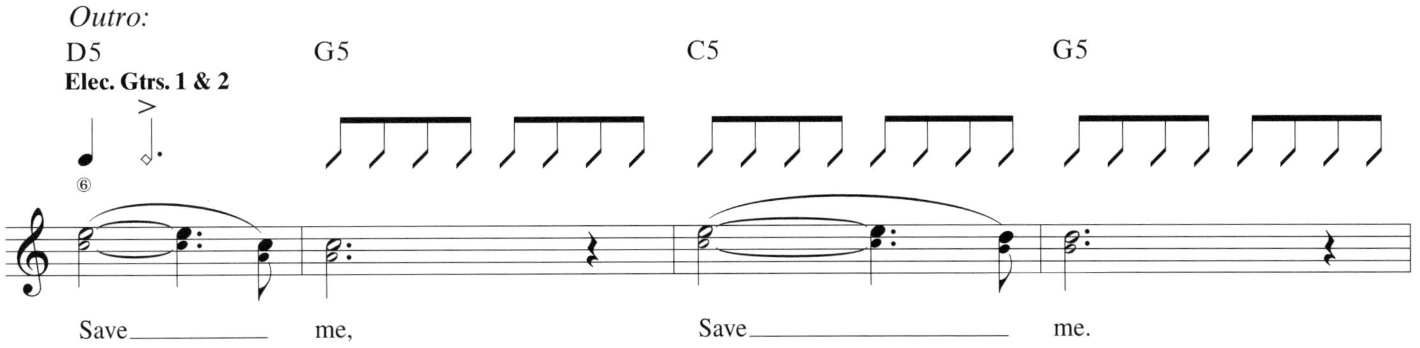
Outro:
D5
G5
C5
G5
Elec. Gtrs. 1 & 2
Save me,
Save me.

D5
F5
C5
tacet
N.C.
Save me,
save…

RIGHT SIDE OF WRONG

Words and Music by
JON BON JOVI

*Composite arrangement.

C C11 C F G Am G
— they think you're pack-in'. Be sure to keep your head down don't look 'em in the eye.
F G Am C/G F
And don't get_ fan - cy, Rick-y, we ain't Jim-my Cag - ney. Look at me, let's do the job and
Chorus:
G C C11 C Dm G
Cont. rhy. simile
let's get home_ to - night._ I got a half_ tank of_ gas_ and if we
Elec. Gtr. 2 (on D.S.)
C C11 C F B C C11 C
run all the lights_ we'll slip a - cross_ the bor - der on the wrong_ side of right._ And

F G Am C/G F
just like Butch and Sun-dance we'll ride un-til the dawn,_ sip-ping whis-key, sing-ing cow-boy songs_
Fm/A♭* To Coda C Em7 F G
Acous. Gtr. 1
_ on the right_ side_ of wrong We picked a
Cont. in slashes
*Played by bass gtr. only.
Verse 2:
C Em7 F G C Am
Piano & Acous. Gtr. 1
Cont. rhy. simile
hell-uv-a night,_ from the shore I see the sky-line. In a cou-ple of hours_ from now,_ Rick, we're gon-na
F G C C9 C7
get out of___ this_ life. We'll stop for smokes, I___ brought a six-pack, we'll stop at
F Am C/G
Look-ers on the way back. Hell, we'll laugh this off,_ keep your fin-gers crossed_ that all___

Chorus:
F G C C11 C Dm G
— goes well ___ to-night. _ I got a half_ tank of_ gas_ and if we
C C11 C F G C C11 C
run all the lights_ we'll slip a-cross_ the bor-der on the wrong_ side of right._ And
F G Am C/G F
just like Butch and Sun-dance we'll ride un-til the dawn,_ sip-ping whis-key, sing-ing cow-boy_
Bridge:
G C E♭5
Elec. Gtr. 2 (w/dist.)
songs on the right_ side_ of wrong. We'll make the grade,_they'll know our names,_ I
B♭5 open F5
need a friend_ to drive._ Here, wear my neck-lace of Saint Chris-to-pher and talk to
C5 5fr E♭5
him while I go in-side.___ I'll take that suit-case, get the cash___ and we'll be gone_
B♭5 F5 F5/A♭
___ be-fore_ you know._ Wait un-til we tell the girls_we're mov-ing down to the Gulf of Mex-i-co.

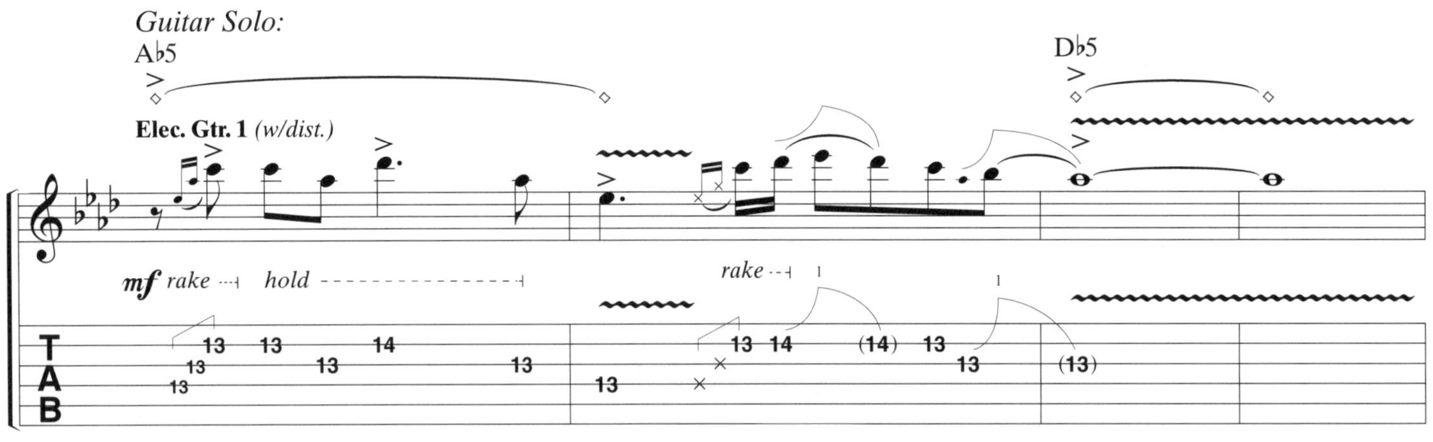
Guitar Solo:
A♭5
D♭5
Elec. Gtr. 1 (w/dist.)
mf rake
hold
rake

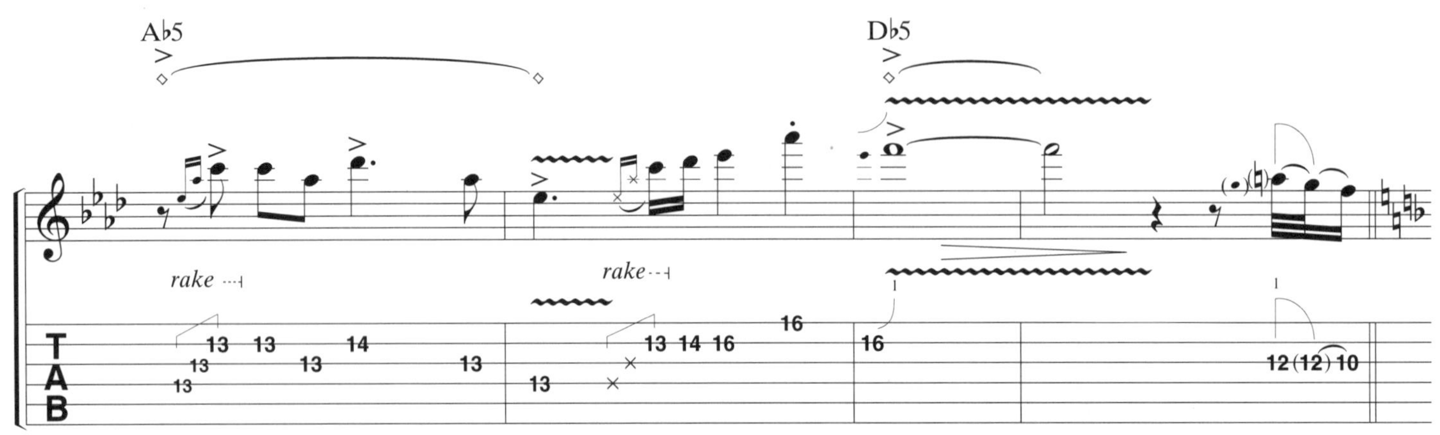
A♭5
D♭5
rake
rake

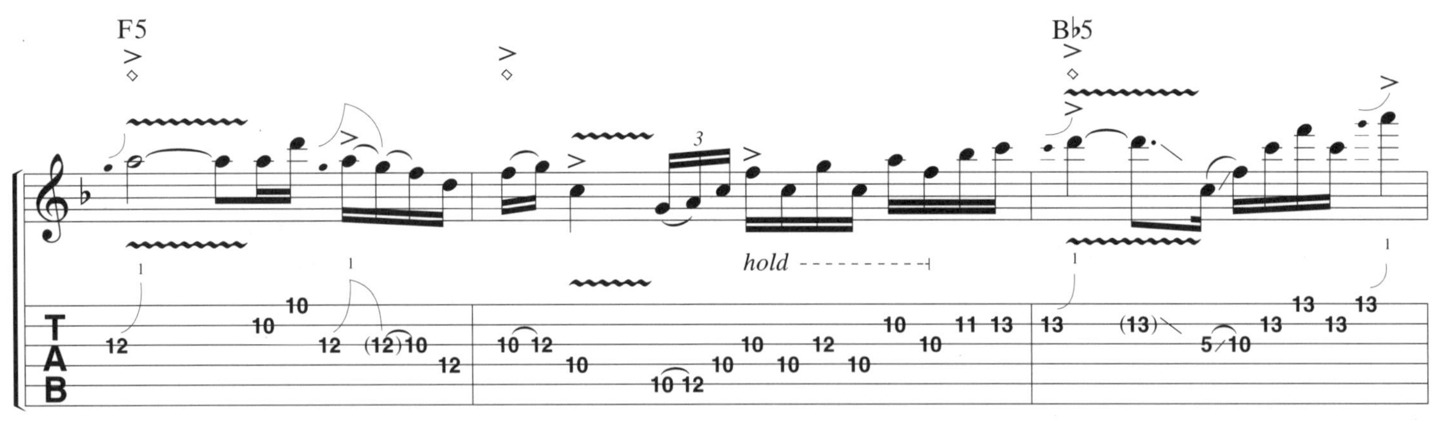
F5
B♭5
hold

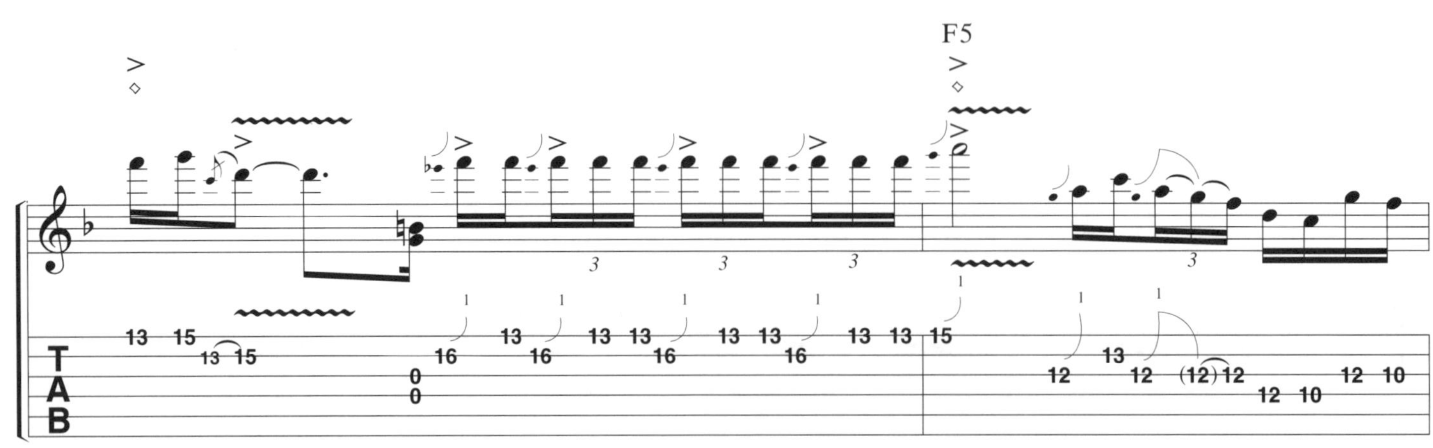
F5

B♭5
D5
C5/E*
F5
G5
rake
C
Em7
F
G
Piano
A friend of a friend needed a favor.
C
Am
F
G
Cont. rhy. simile
Life was just what happened while we were busy making plans. We never saw

C
C7
F
Fm
noth - ing, there was a run - in'. A nine mil - li - me - ter steel was com - ing for the

D.S. 𝄋 al Coda
Am
C/G
F
C
C7
wind - shield of that Olds - mo - bile as the cops said, "Show your hands". I got a

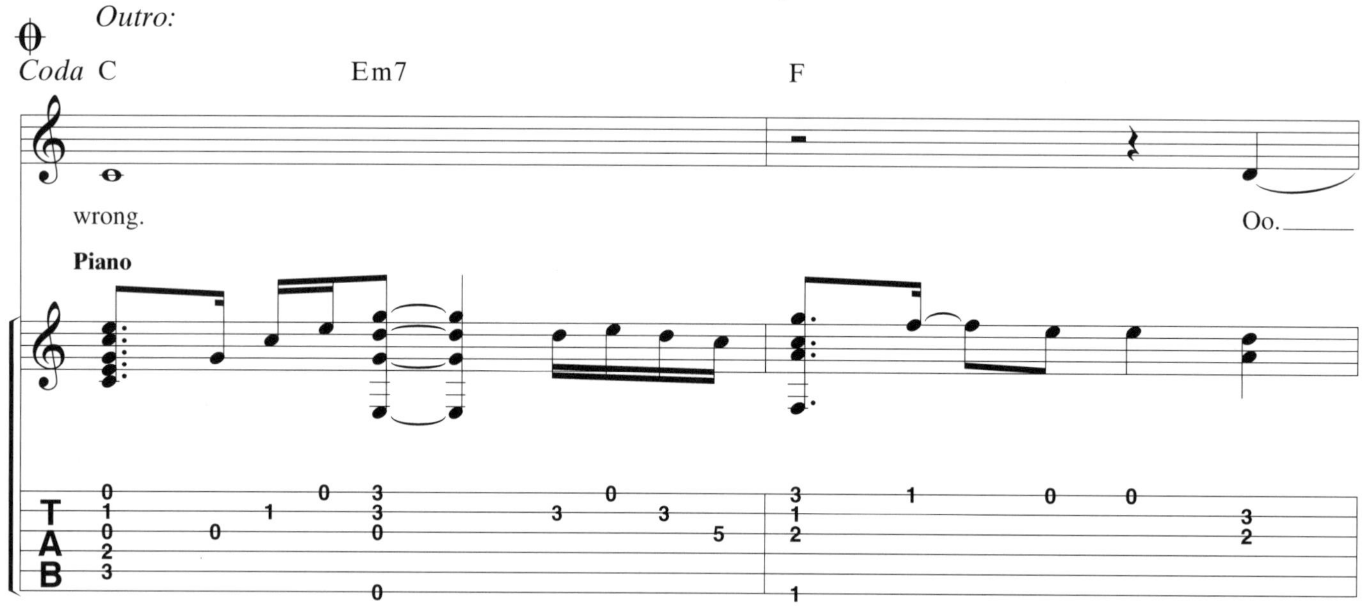
Outro:
Coda C
Em7
F
wrong.
Oo.
Piano

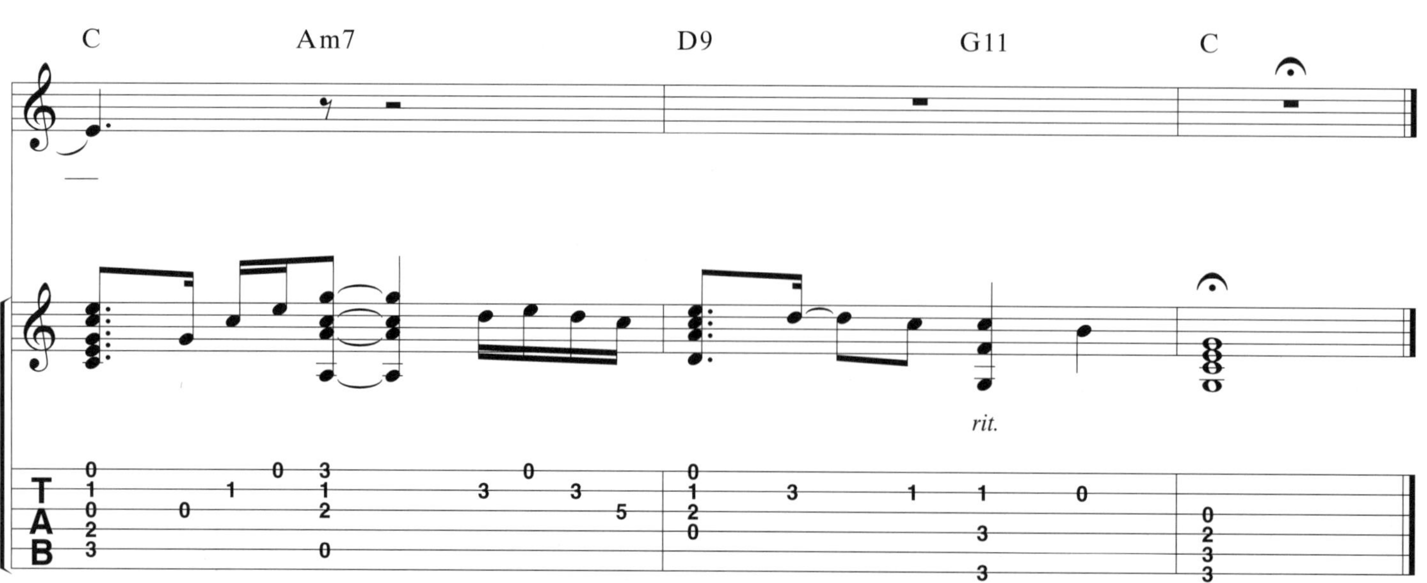
C
Am7
D9
G11
C
rit.

LOVE ME BACK TO LIFE

Words and Music by
JON BON JOVI and RICHIE SAMBORA

All gtrs. w/Drop D tuning: ⑥ = D

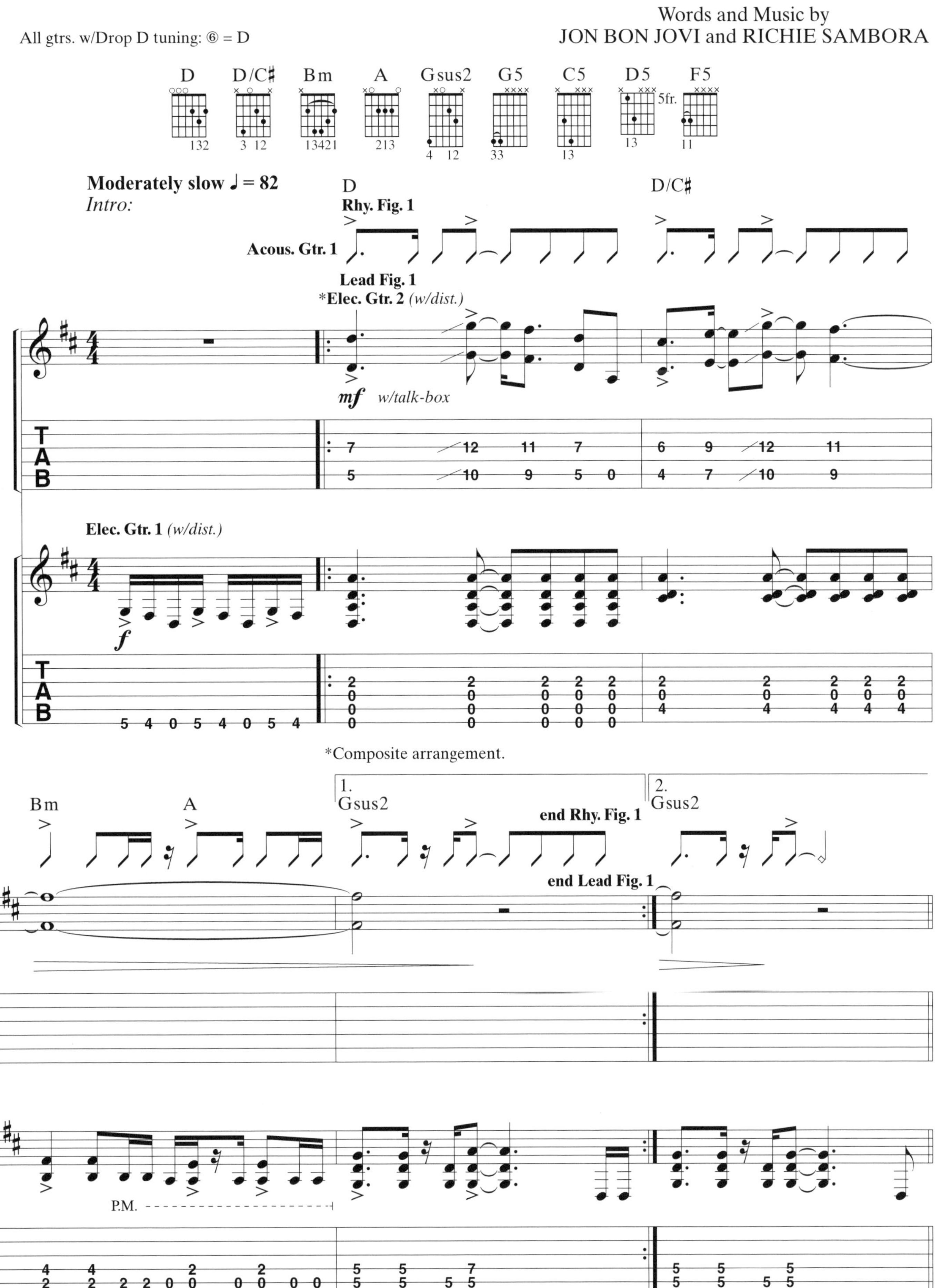

*Composite arrangement.

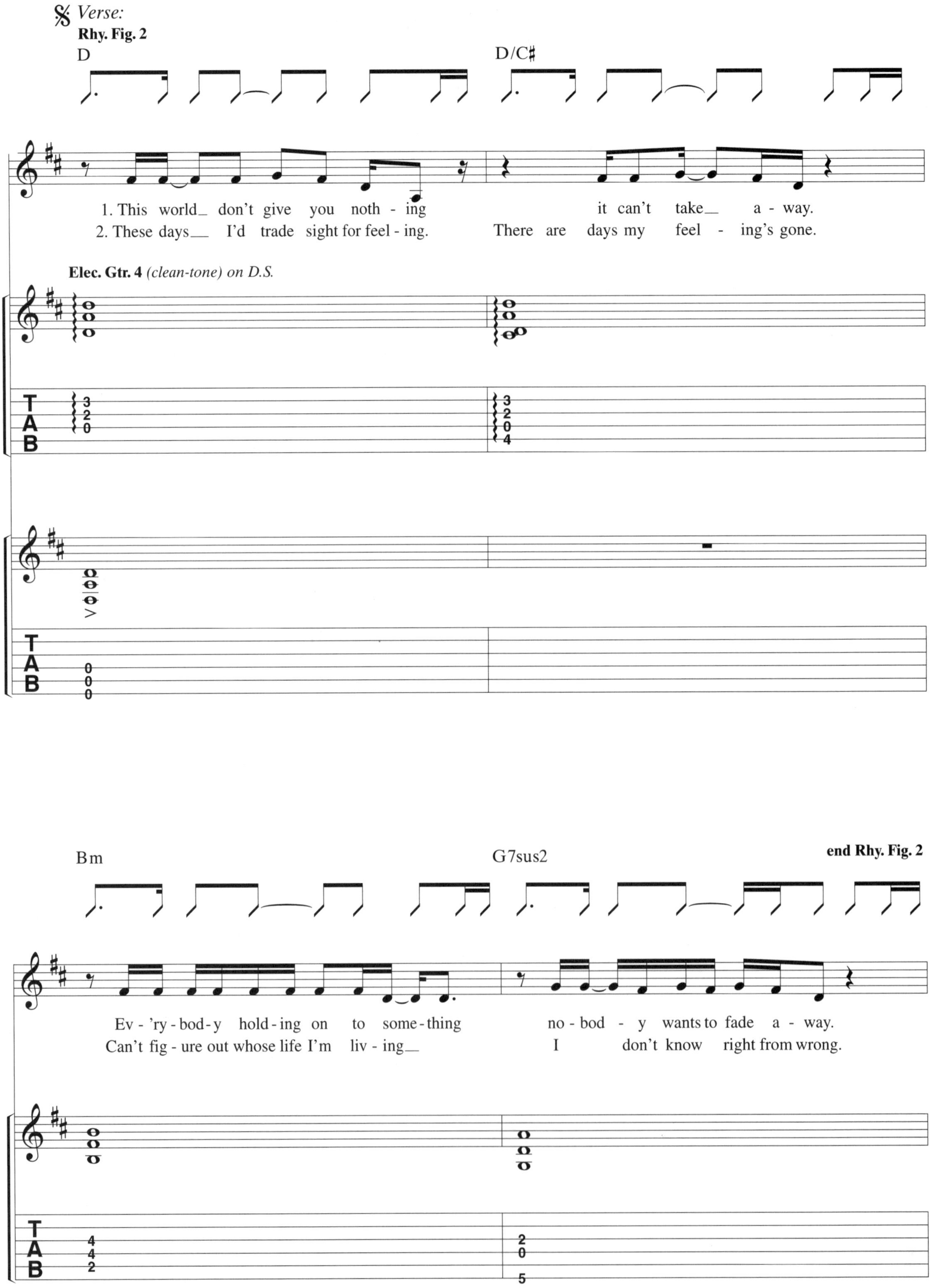

𝄋 *Verse:*

Rhy. Fig. 2

D D/C♯

1. This world_ don't give you noth - ing it can't take_ a - way.
2. These days_ I'd trade sight for feel - ing. There are days my feel - ing's gone.

Elec. Gtr. 4 *(clean-tone) on D.S.*

T
A
B

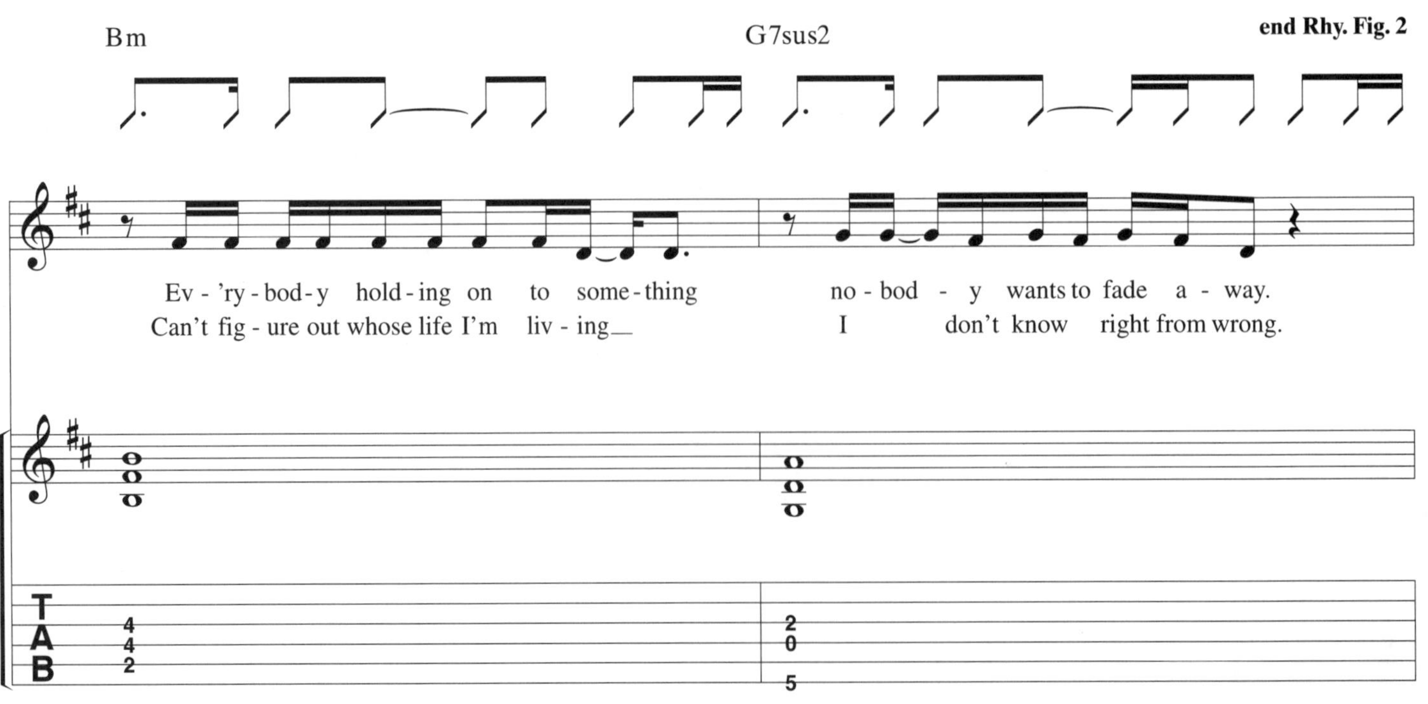

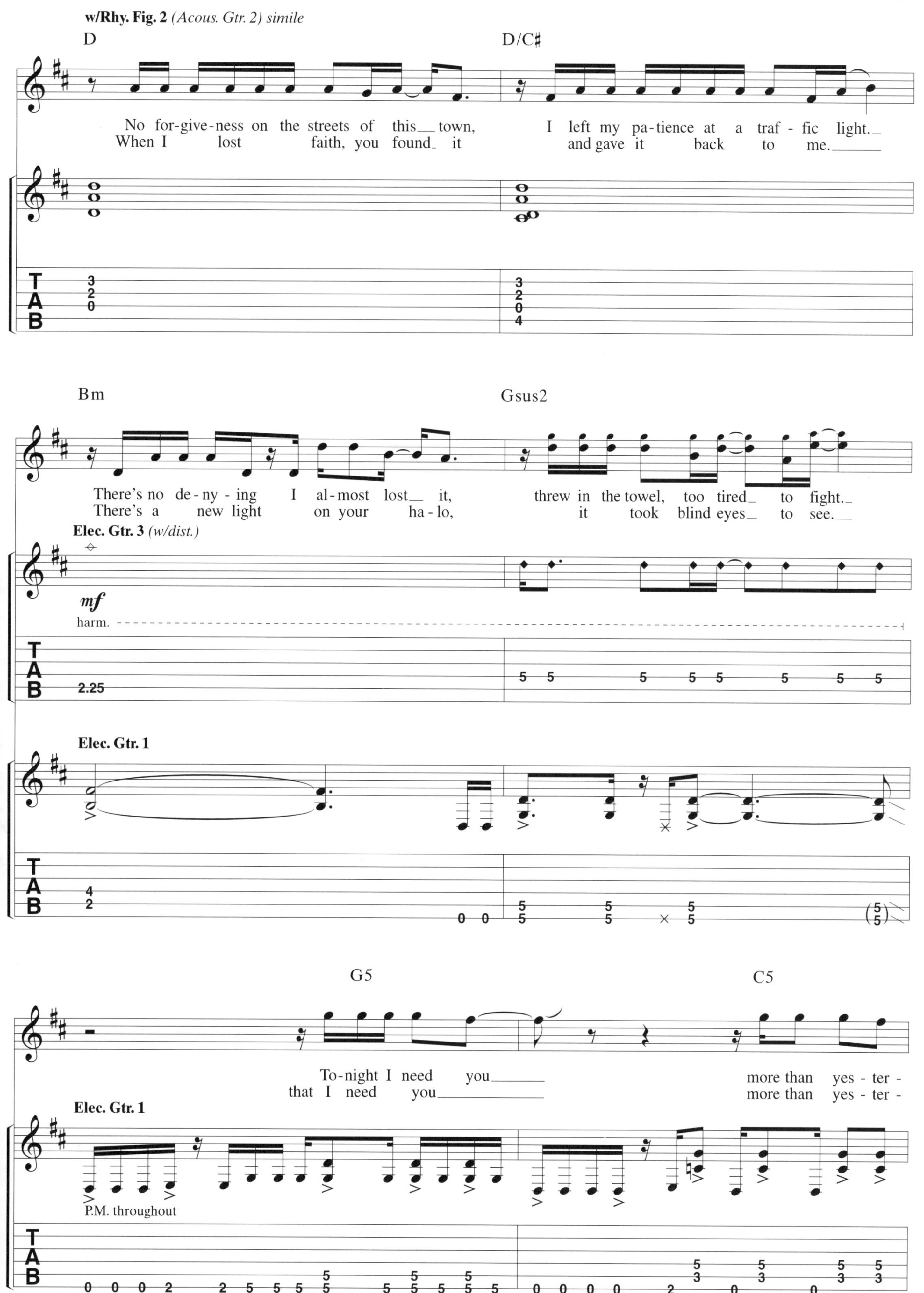
w/Rhy. Fig. 2 (Acous. Gtr. 2) simile
D
D/C♯
No for-give-ness on the streets of this__ town,
When I lost faith, you found_ it
I left my pa-tience at a traf - fic light._
and gave it back to me.______
Bm
Gsus2
There's no de-ny - ing I al-most lost__ it,
There's a new light on your ha-lo,
threw in the towel, too tired_ to fight._
it took blind eyes_ to see.__
Elec. Gtr. 3 (w/dist.)
mf
harm.
Elec. Gtr. 1
G5
C5
To-night I need you______
that I need you__________
more than yes - ter -
more than yes - ter -
Elec. Gtr. 1
P.M. throughout

𝄋𝄋 Chorus:
w/Rhy. Fig. 1 (Acous. Gtr. 1) 1 3/4 times, simile
G5
N.C.
D
day._ To-night I need you._____
day._ Yeah, I need you._____
Take me,_ touch_ me, hold me
Rhy. Fig. 1A
P.M. throughout
hold
D/C♯
Bm
A
Gsus2
like you_ mean_ it.
Make me come_ a - live.__
end Rhy. Fig. 1A
(hold)
w/Rhy. Fig. 1A (Elec. Gtr. 1) 1st 3 bars, simile
D
D/C♯
Bm
A
To Coda
Hurt me,_ heal_ me, come and make me_ feel__ it.
Res-cue me_ to - night._
1.
Gsus2
D.S. 𝄋
2.
G7sus2
Acous. Gtr. 1
Acous. Gtr. 1
__ Love me back_ to life.____
__ Love me back_ to life.
Elec. Gtr. 1
Elec. Gtr. 1

Guitar Solo:
C5
D5
C5
D5
*Elec. Gtrs. 1 & 2
*Composite arrangement.
C5
G5
F5
C5
D5
Elec. Gtr. 3
mf
C5
N.C.

Chorus:
w/Rhy. Fig. 1 (Acous. Gtr. 1) 2 times, simile
D
D/C♯
Bm
A
Gsus2
Take me, touch me, hold me like you mean it. Make me come alive.
D
D/C♯
D.S.S. al Coda
Hurt me, heal me, come on, make me feel it! Rescue me. Come on
Elec. Gtr. 1
*Strings.
Coda
Gsus2
Elec. Gtr. 1 & Acous. Gtr. 1
4fr
Outro:
w/Rhy. Figs. 1 (Acous. Gtr. 1) & 1A (Elec. Gtr. 1) simile
D
D/C♯
Love me back to-night.
Come on, love me back to life.
Bm
A
1. Gsus2
2. G5
Elec. Gtr. 1
Love me back to life. Oo.

YOU HAD ME FROM HELLO

Words and Music by
JON BON JOVI, RICHIE SAMBORA and ANDREAS CARLSSON

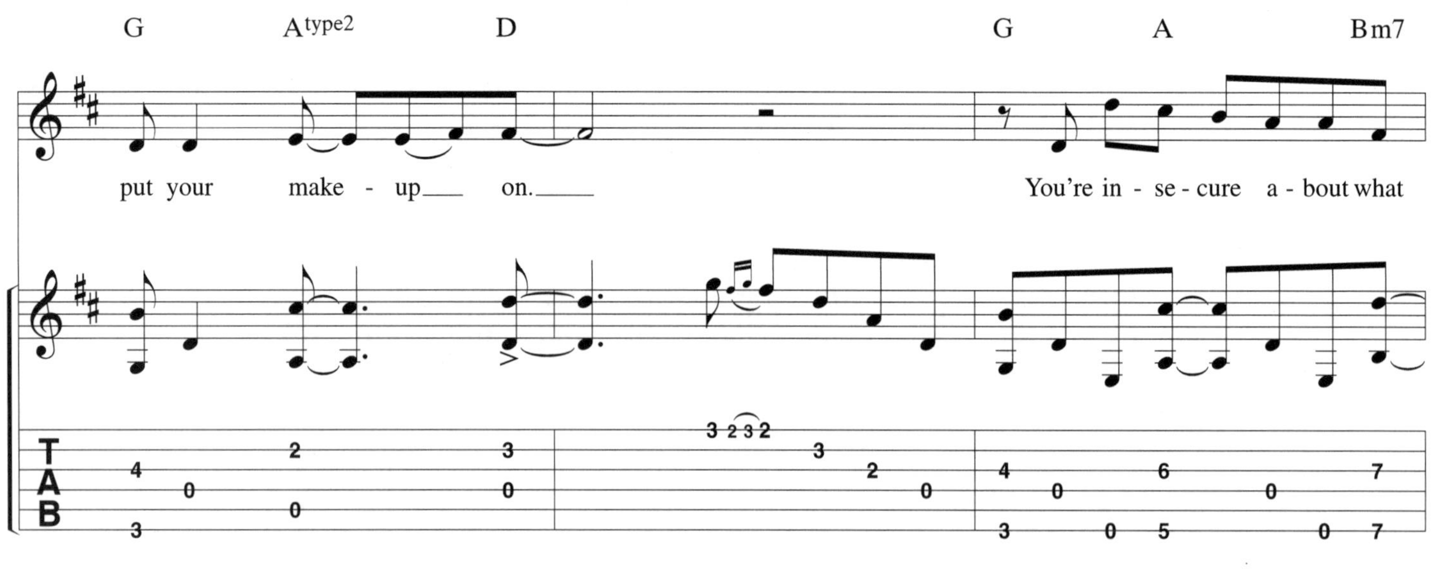
G
Atype2
D
G
A
Bm7
put your make - up on.
You're in - se - cure a - bout what

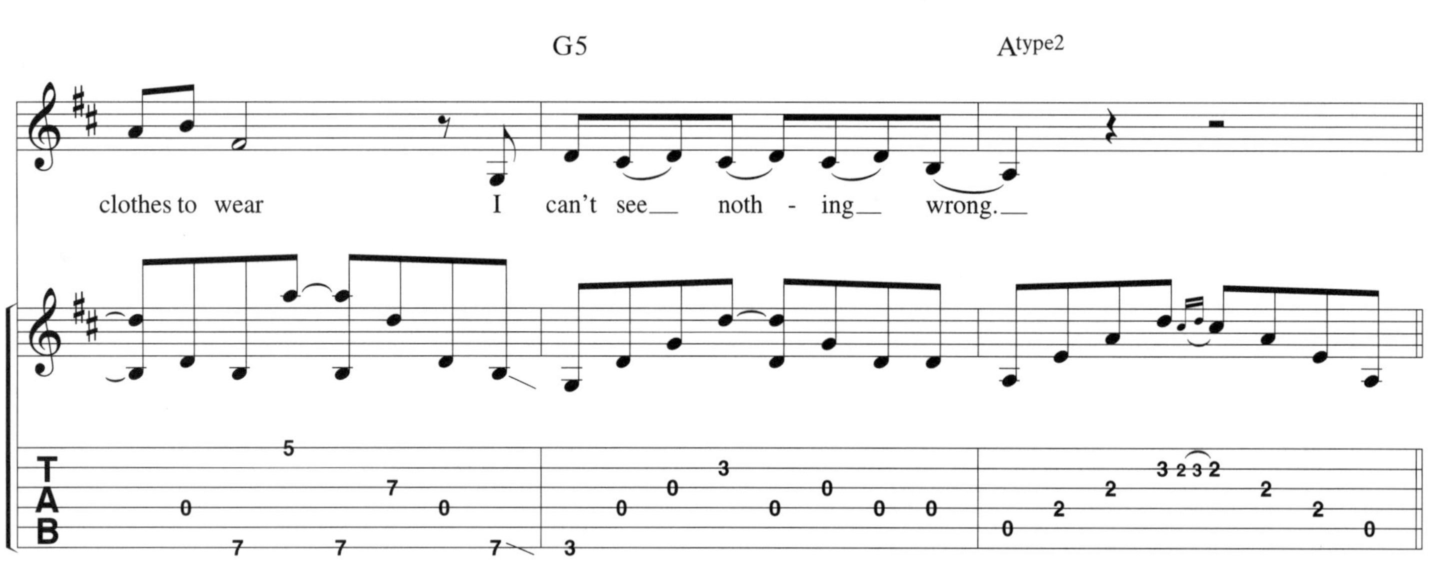
G5
Atype2
clothes to wear I can't see noth - ing wrong.

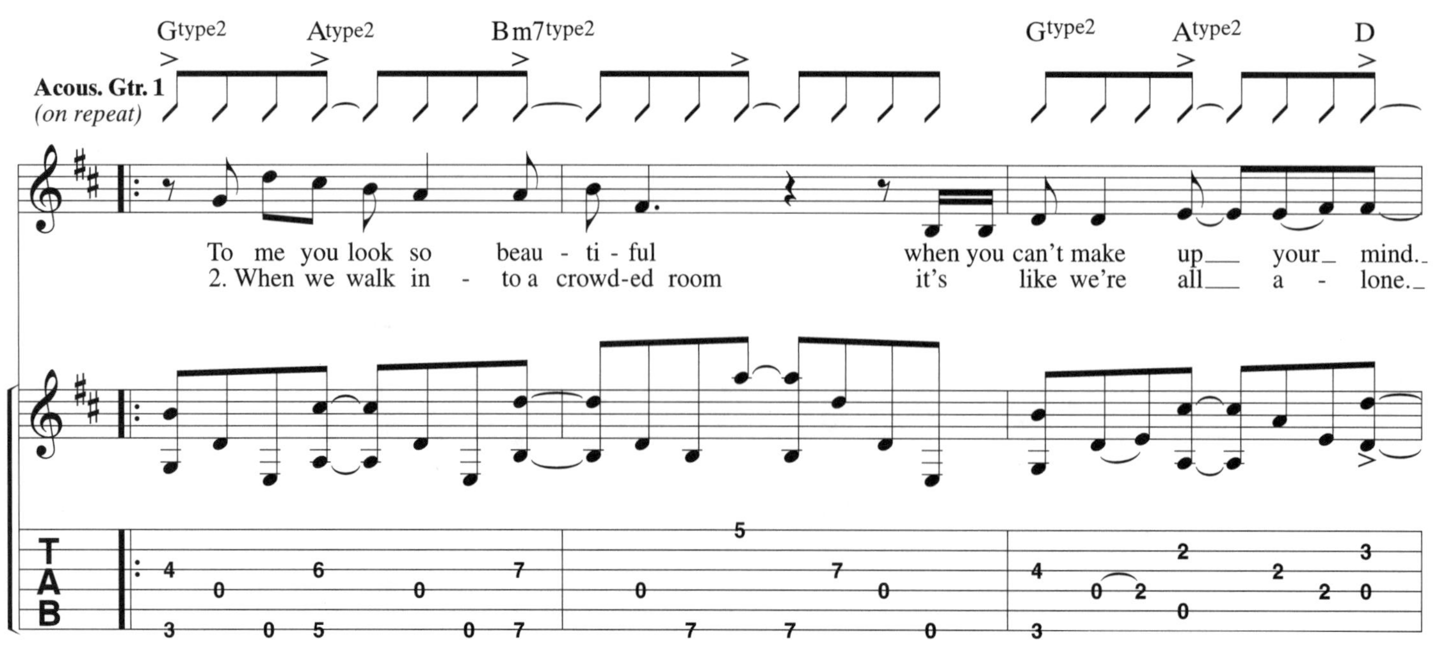
Gtype2
Atype2
Bm7type2
Gtype2
Atype2
D
Acous. Gtr. 1
(on repeat)
To me you look so beau - ti - ful when you can't make up your mind.
2. When we walk in - to a crowd-ed room it's like we're all a - lone.

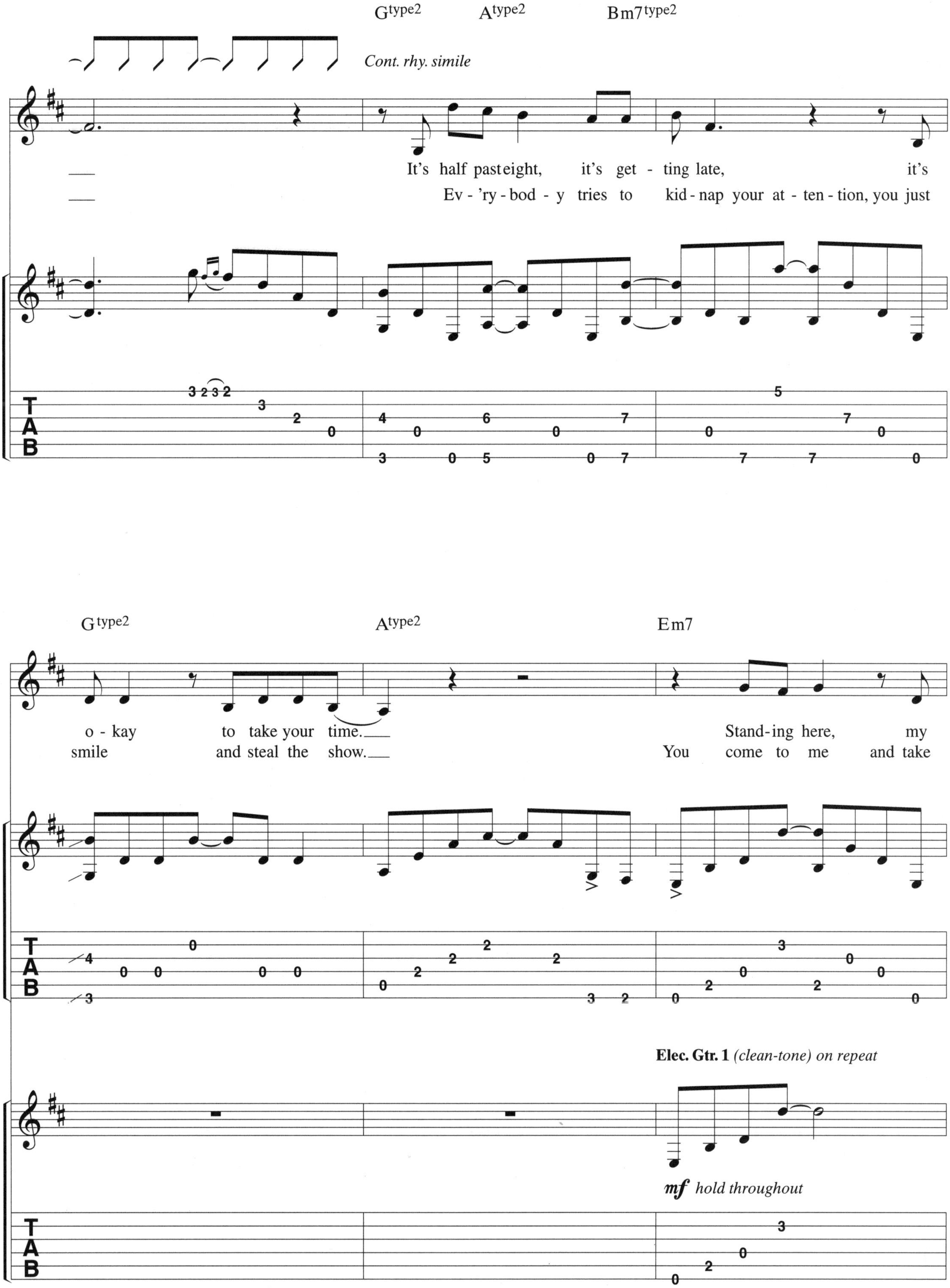

G type2 A type2 Em7

o - kay to take your time. Stand - ing here, my

smile and steal the show. You come to me and take

Elec. Gtr. 1 *(clean-tone) on repeat*

mf *hold throughout*

D/F♯
Gsus2
Atype2
D/A
A7
hands in my pock-ets like I have_ a thou - sand times.
my hand, we start danc - in' slow.
T
A
B
Em7
Acous. Gtr. 3 (12-string)
D/F♯
Gtype2
Think-ing back, it took_ one_ breath,_ one word_ to change_ my life._
You put your lips up to_ my_ ear_ and whis-per way_ down low._

𝄋 Chorus:

Atype2 D(9)/F♯ Bm(11) G6sus2

*Acous. Gtrs. 1 & 2

The first___ time_ I saw___ you_ it felt_ like com-ing home._
From the

Elec. Gtr. 1 (on repeat)

Cont. in slashes hold throughout

Acous. Gtr. 2 (on D.S.)

hold throughout

*Composite arrangement.

Atype2 Asus2 D(9)/F♯ G6sus2

Cont. rhy. simile

If I____ nev - er__ told___ you_ I just want you to know,_

*Composite arrangement.

C
F
lay - ing down be - side me
Elec. Gtr. 1 (clean-tone)
mf
Dm
Gsus
Gtype2
I feel your heart beat to re - mind me.
Guitar Solo:
D(9)/F♯
Bm(11)
G6sus2
Atype2 Asus2
Acous. Gtr. 1 & Elec. Gtrs. 1 & 2
Cont. rhy. simile
Elec. Gtr. 3 (clean-tone)
mf
harm.
hold throughout

D.S. 𝄋 al Coda
D(9)/F♯
G6sus2
Atype2
Asus2
The
(harm.)
Coda
Outro:
G
A
Bm7
Ah,
Acous. Gtr. 1
Acous. Gtr. 2
G
Atype2
D/F♯
From
hel - lo.
rit.
Acous. Gtr. 3
rit.

BOUNCE

Words and Music by
JON BON JOVI, RICHIE SAMBORA and BILLY FALCON

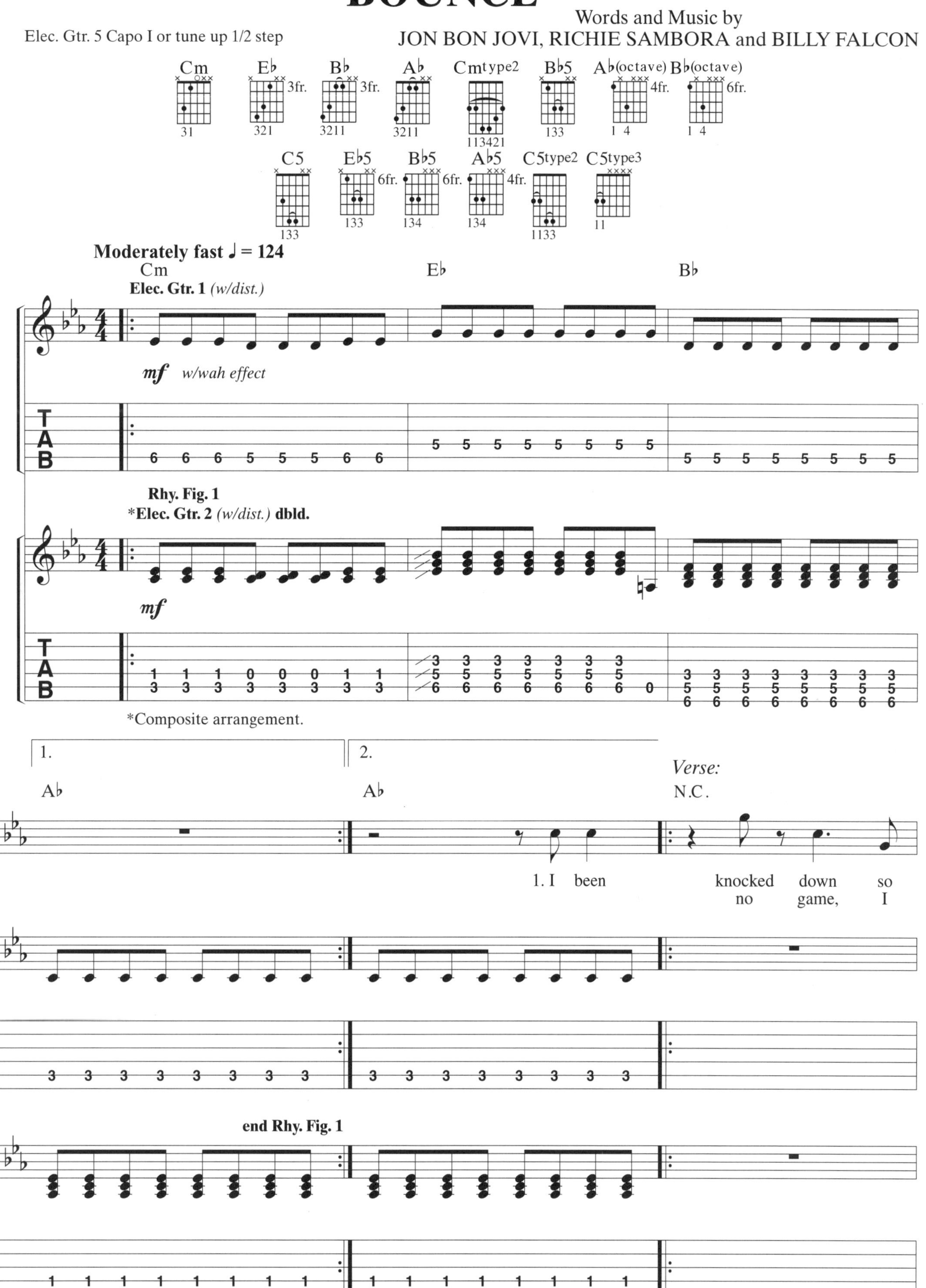

Cm type2
Elec. Gtr. 3
(w/dist.)
many times. Count-ed out six, sev-en, eight, nine.
play it hard. Kicked a-round, cut, stitched, and scarred. I'll
Elec. Gtr. 4 (clean-tone)
Writ-ten off like some bad deal. If you're breath-ing you know
take the hit but not the fall. I know no fear, still
1.
B♭
A♭
B♭
how it feels. Call it Kar-ma, call it luck, me, I just don't
Elec. Gtr. 1
Elec. Gtr. 2

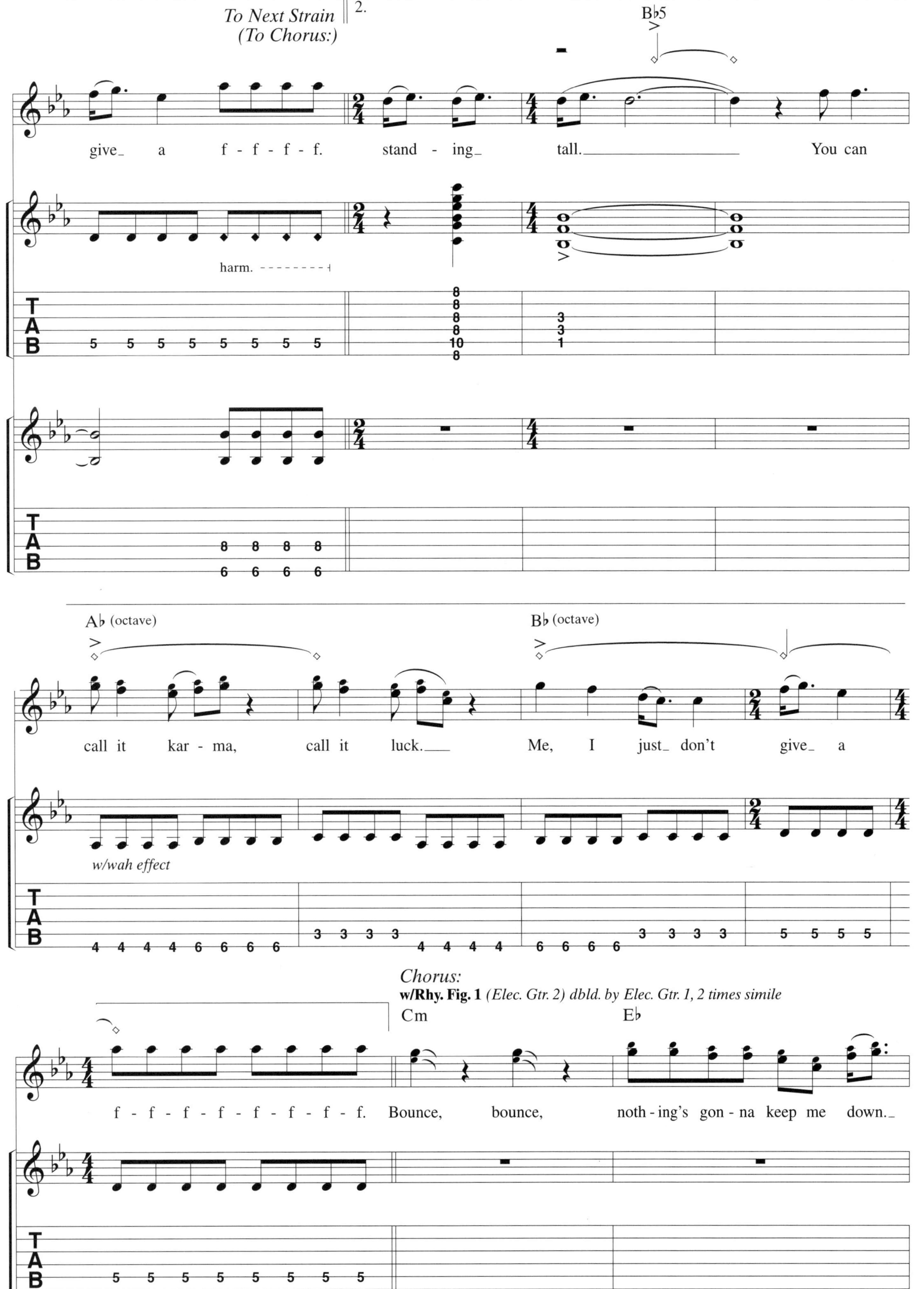
To Next Strain
(To Chorus:)
2.
B♭5
give_ a f - f - f - f. stand - ing_ tall._ You can
harm.
Ab (octave)
B♭ (octave)
call it kar - ma, call it luck._ Me, I just_ don't give_ a
w/wah effect
Chorus:
w/Rhy. Fig. 1 (Elec. Gtr. 2) dbld. by Elec. Gtr. 1, 2 times simile
Cm
E♭
f - f - f - f - f - f - f - f. Bounce, bounce, noth - ing's gon - na keep me down._

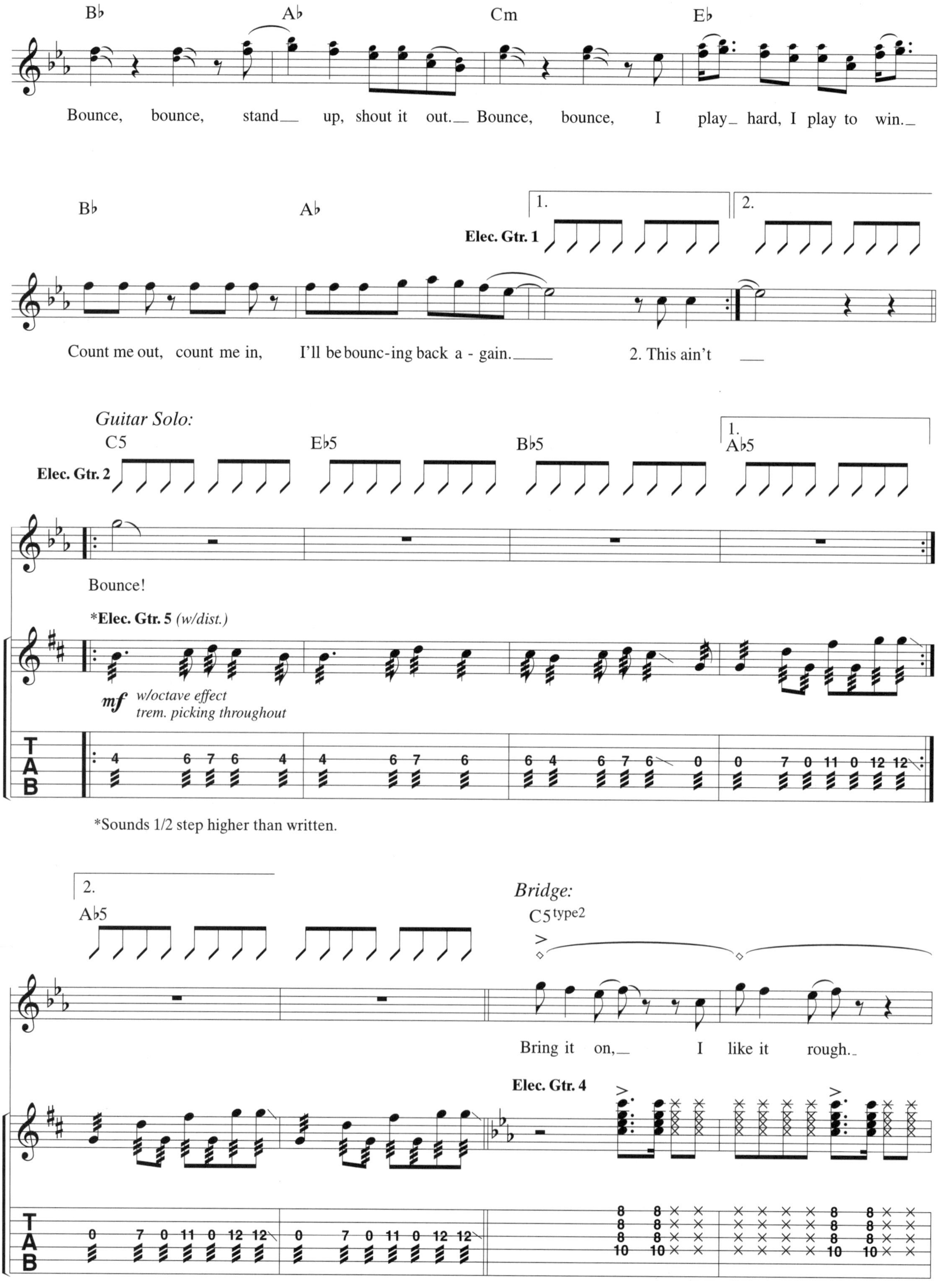

B♭ A♭ Cm E♭
Bounce, bounce, stand up, shout it out. Bounce, bounce, I play hard, I play to win.
B♭ A♭
1. 2.
Elec. Gtr. 1
Count me out, count me in, I'll be bounc-ing back a - gain. 2. This ain't
Guitar Solo:
C5 E♭5 B♭5 1. A♭5
Elec. Gtr. 2
Bounce!
*Elec. Gtr. 5 (w/dist.)
mf w/octave effect
trem. picking throughout
*Sounds 1/2 step higher than written.
2. A♭5
Bridge:
C5 type2
Bring it on, I like it rough.
Elec. Gtr. 4

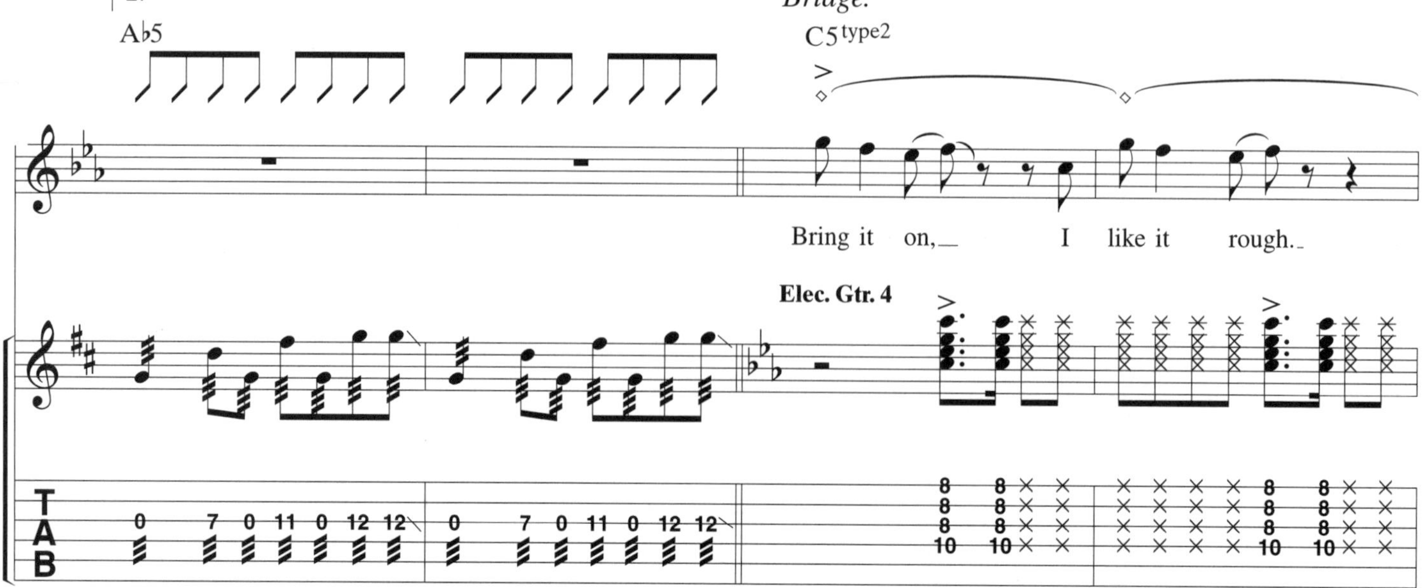

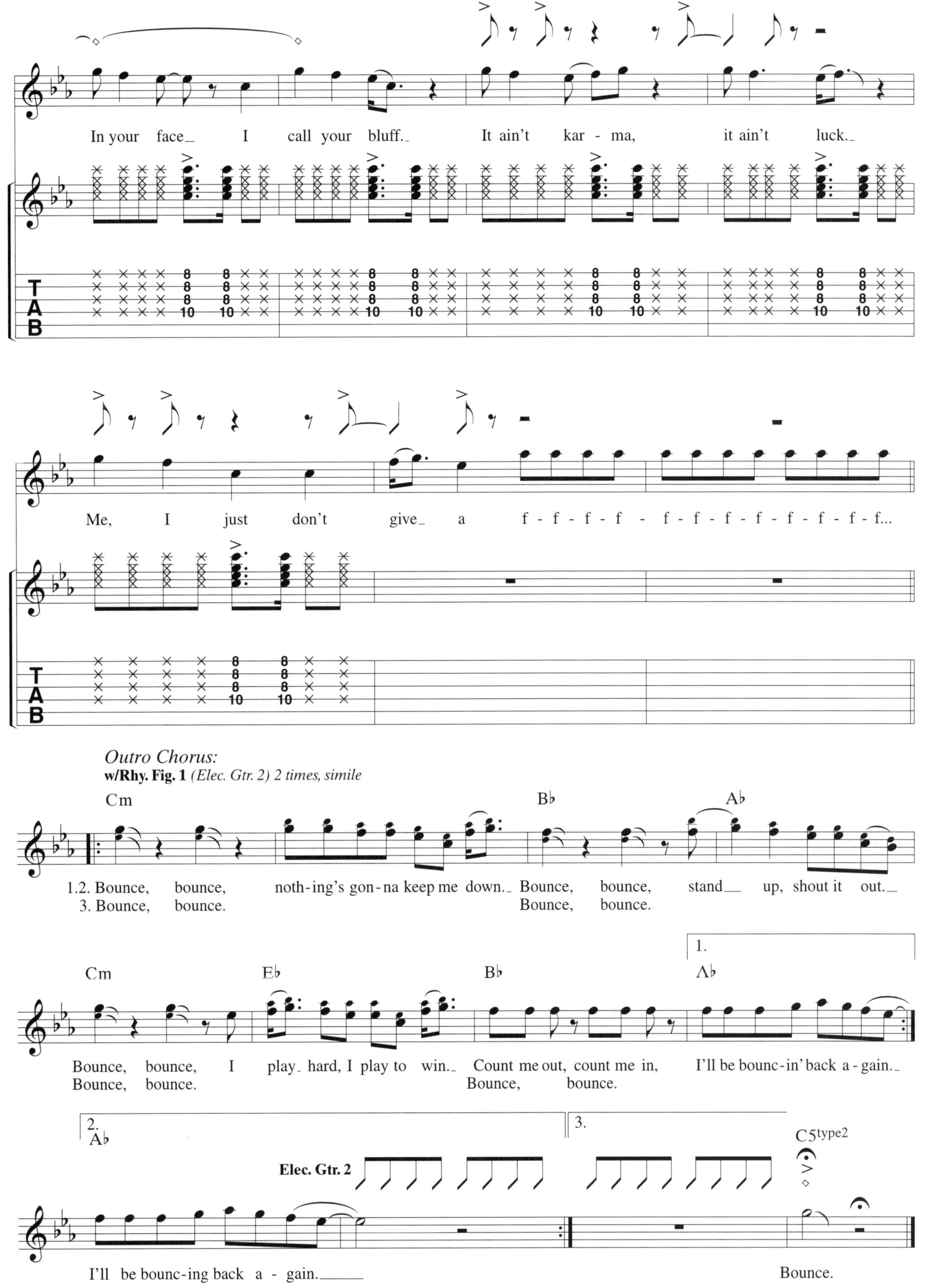
In your face I call your bluff. It ain't karma, it ain't luck.
Me, I just don't give a f-f-f-f-f-f-f-f-f-f-f-f...
Outro Chorus:
w/Rhy. Fig. 1 (Elec. Gtr. 2) 2 times, simile
Cm
Bb
Ab
1.2. Bounce, bounce, noth-ing's gon-na keep me down. Bounce, bounce, stand up, shout it out.
3. Bounce, bounce. Bounce, bounce.
Cm
Eb
Bb
1.
Ab
Bounce, bounce, I play hard, I play to win. Count me out, count me in, I'll be bounc-in' back a-gain.
Bounce, bounce. Bounce, bounce.
2.
Ab
Elec. Gtr. 2
3.
C5type2
I'll be bounc-ing back a-gain.
Bounce.

OPEN ALL NIGHT

Words and Music by
JON BON JOVI and RICHIE SAMBORA

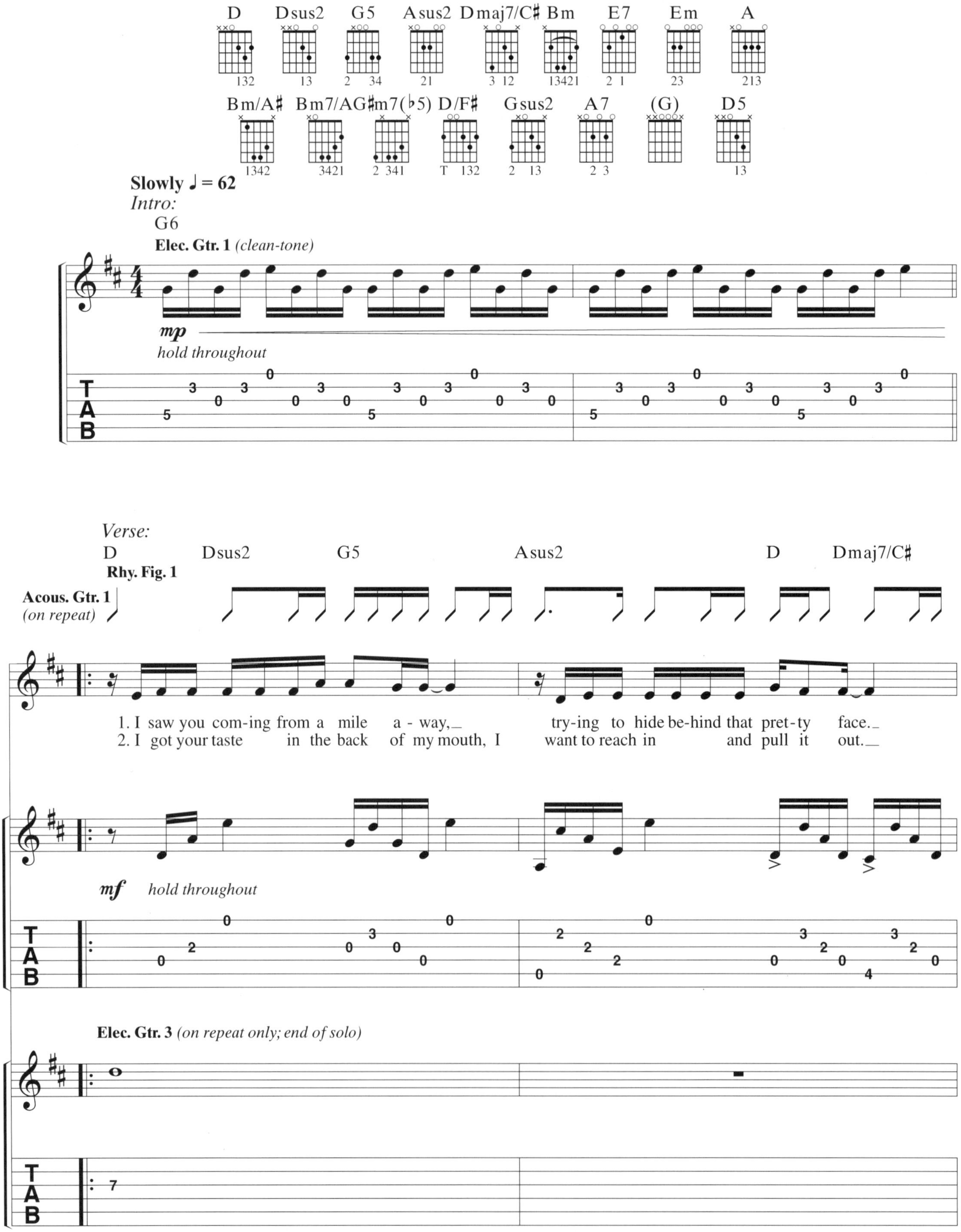

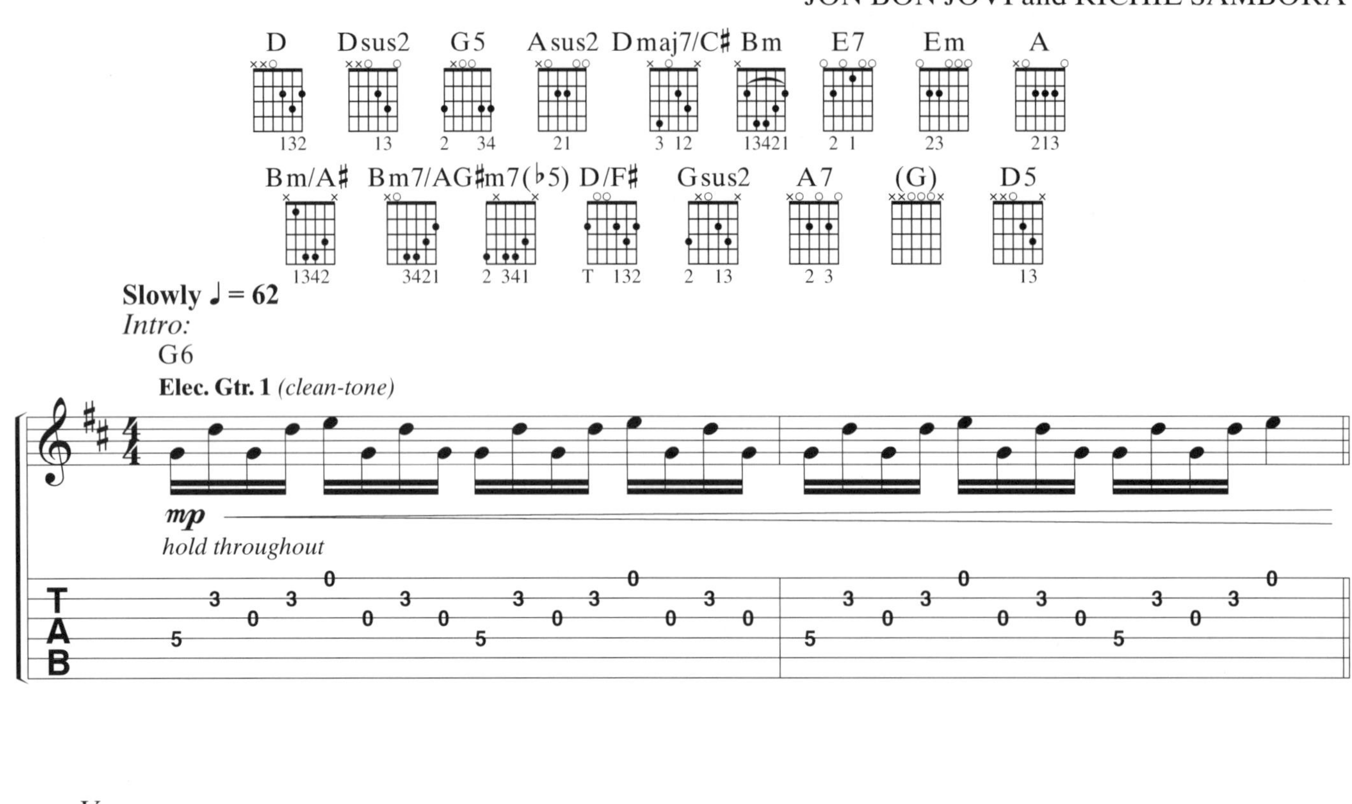

Verse:

D Dsus2 G5 Asus2 D Dmaj7/C♯

Rhy. Fig. 1

Acous. Gtr. 1 *(on repeat)*

1. I saw you com-ing from a mile a - way,_ try-ing to hide be-hind that pret-ty face._
2. I got your taste in the back of my mouth, I want to reach in and pull it out._

mf *hold throughout*

Elec. Gtr. 3 *(on repeat only; end of solo)*

Bm
E7
Em
A
Asus2
end Rhy. Fig. 1
Bet my last dol-lar, ba-by, you've been bruised._ Poor___ lit - tle heart,_ all black 'n' blue._
And I'd be ly-ing if I did - n't say when you're this close,_ I'm a - fraid_
w/Rhy. Fig. 1 (Acous. Gtr. 1) simile (on repeat)
D
Dsus2
G5
Asus2
D
Dmaj7/C♯
Last thing you need's an-oth-er pick - up line,__ you must have heard them all a thou-sand times._
of the way I'll feel if I touch your hair,__ the way I'll miss you when you're not there,_
Bm
E7
Em
A
Asus2
God on-ly knows what you've been through,_ be-lieve me I___ been bro - ken too.__
and that I'll see you when I close my eyes.___ it's too late,_ I've_crossed that line.

Bm Bm/A♯* Bm/A** G♯m7(♭5)/E†

Rhy. Fig. 2A

Acous. Gtr. 1

It aches, it breaks, it takes your breath a - way. I've

Rhy. Fig. 2

Piano *(arr. for gtr.)*

mf *hold throughout*

*Bass gtr. plays C♯. **Bass gtr. plays D. †Bass gtr. plays E.

Chorus:

G5 A Asus2 D/F♯ G5

mf

end Rhy. Fig. 2

Acous. Gtr. 1

been a-round that block a time or two. Ba - by. I don't want to

I'll still be a-round come clos - ing time.

**Elec. Gtr. 1 (dbld.) by Elec. Gtr. 2 *(clean-tone)*

**Composite arrangement.

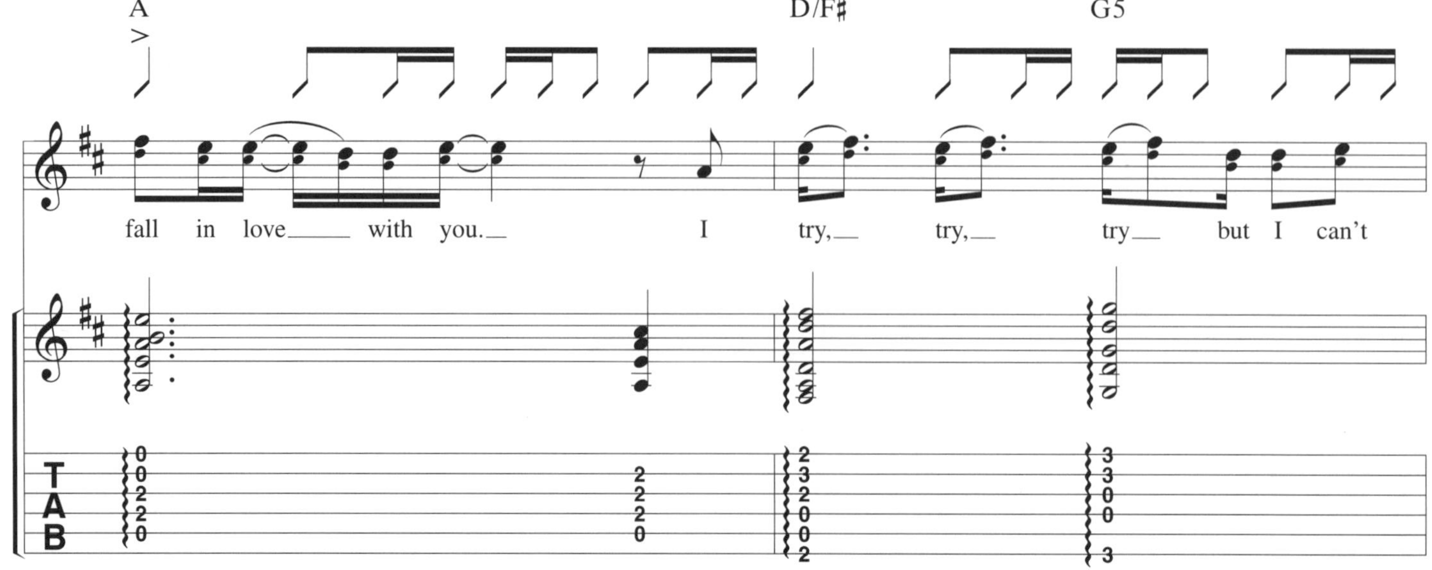

A
Bm
Bm/A♯
Acous. Gtr. 1 tacet
get a - round the truth. Please don't say my name, give this heart a break, I don't want to
hold
Bm/A
G♯m7(♭5)
G5
Asus2
make the same mis-take. But it's too late, I'll leave on the light. These arms are o-pen all
(hold)
1.
Interlude:
Gsus2
D
G5
Em
A
A7
2. Guitar Solo:
D
G5
Acous. Gtr. 1
night.
night.
Elec. Gtr. 3 (w/dist.)
Elec. Gtr. 3
Piano
hold throughout

Em
Asus2
D
G5
Em
Asus2
w/Rhy. Figs. 2 (Piano) & 2A (Acous. Gtr. 1) simile
Bm
Bm/A♯
Bm/A
G♯m7(♭5)
G5
It's two a. m., it's last call, ba - by.
The bar - keep's gone, I'll walk you home, now.
Save me,
A
A7
Outro Chorus:
D/F♯
G5
A
Acous. Gtr. 1
ba - by.
I don't want to
fall in love with you.
I

D/F♯
G5
A
G
try__ try,__ try,__ but I can't get a - round_ the truth. Please don't make me
Acous. Gtr. 1 tacet
Bm
Bm/A♯
Bm/A
G♯m7(♭5)
beg,_ give this heart a break._ I don't want to make the same_ mis - take.__ But it's too
hold
Elec. Gtrs. 1 & 2 tacet
G5
Asus2
Gsus2
D5
Acous. Gtr. 1
late, I'll leave on__ the light.__ These arms are o - pen_ all__ night.__
Piano

BON JOVI
BOUNCE